D0991610

Some other books by Jean Lee Latham

ON STAGE, MR. JEFFERSON!

THIS DEAR-BOUGHT LAND

CARRY ON, MR. BOWDITCH

TRAIL BLAZER OF THE SEAS

Young Man in a Hurry

by *Jean Lee Latham*

Winner of the 1955 Newbery Award

Pictures by *Victor Mays*

Harper & Row, Publishers · New York and Evanston

Young Man in a Hurry

THE STORY OF CYRUS W. FIELD

Young Man in a Hurry

Printed in the United States of America

Library of Congress catalog card number: 58–7761

I-Q

To

ELLEN

who opened doors to research for it

JULIE

who thought of the name for it

URSULA

who piloted it into port

Contents

Young Man in a Hurry

Chapter 1

Stranger in a Strange Land

CYRUS SHARPENED A QUILL AND OPENED THE FAMILY account book to the page headed "April 1835." He sorted the scraps of paper with expenses jotted on them and began to write:

Letter from Dudley 13 cents

Letters cost a lot, but that one from his brother had been worth every penny:

. . . Yes, fifteen years old is a little young to tackle New York City, but if Cyrus is determined to be a business man, I suppose the best thing is for him to come to New York and get a job in a successful store. Perhaps in A. T. Stewart's. That's the biggest dry-goods store in New York —probably in America. New York is certainly the business center of the country now. Ever since the Erie Canal opened we've been growing by leaps and bounds. Too bad Cyrus doesn't want to be a lawyer. If he did . . .

He stopped thinking of Dudley's letter and picked up another slip. He wrote:

To Stephen and Henry 50 cents each 1 dollar

It's costing Father plenty to keep two sons in college. I'd think he'd be glad I'll be on my own and taking care of myself.

But Father wasn't glad. That look in his eyes . . .

He shook off that thought, too, and made the last three entries. When he had finished he drew a line across the page and wrote:

End of account kept by Cyrus W. Field
Tuesday, April 28, 1835.

Who'd be doing this tomorrow, he wondered, when he was on his way to New York? Father? He grinned. Father would start thinking of a sermon and forget. Poor Mother—she always said she had no head for figures, but she'd have to take care of it again.

If only he could get back once in a while. But he thought of the long journey from Stockbridge to New York. Fifty miles by horse and buggy to the Hudson River—that would take all day. The boat trip down-river—that would take all night. Thursday morning before he'd be in New York. And the expense! Two dollars! No, he couldn't make that trip very often!

Mother came to the door. "I'm sorry, Cyrus, but you'll have to go to the store again. I forgot the buttons for your new suit."

If only he could say, "No! Please don't send me!" If only he could tell her what it was like to go to the store now—how everybody wanted to "have a few words" with him:

"I thought you'd be a lawyer, like Dudley."

"Why aren't you going to be a minister, like your father?"

"You mean you aren't going to enter a profession?"

But he couldn't tell Mother about that. He smiled and hurried out. Maybe if I walk fast and look straight ahead nobody will notice me. Maybe—

He hadn't gone half a block when someone yelled from across the street. "You there, Cyrus! I want to talk to you!"

He groaned when he saw the pudgy little man, fists on hips, chin outthrust. "Old Mark-My-Words" was what the boys of Stockbridge called Mr. Holderby. Even the grownups said he was the most opinionated man in Massachusetts and tried to duck when they saw him coming. But a boy had to say "Yes, Mr. Holderby!" and listen. Especially when the boy was a preacher's son.

Cyrus picked his way across the muddy road. "Yes, Mr. Holderby?"

"What's all this nonsense about you going to New York?"

Cyrus tried to explain.

Mr. Holderby broke in. "Bah! Mark my words, Cyrus! You'd come crawling home in mighty short order! It's no place for you! And I'm going to tell your father so! Right now!"

When Cyrus got back from the store the door to

Father's study was closed, but the first sound he heard was "Mark my words, Dr. Field!" He hesitated, then went upstairs where Mother was sewing.

"Mr. Holderby certainly is on a tear," she said. "I wonder what's on his mind?"

Cyrus didn't explain. He sat down and watched her working the buttonholes in his new suit. "I'm sorry I'm growing so fast."

Mother smiled. "I'm not. I like my tall sons."

"We put you to a lot of trouble—always growing out of our clothes."

"That's the only trouble. Not a one of you has ever given me a minute's heartache."

From downstairs Mr. Holderby's voice exploded again. "Mark my words, Dr. Field!"

"Funny," Cyrus muttered. "People ask a preacher's advice about everything else in the world. Then *they* try to tell *him* how to raise his own children. Especially boys."

"Cyrus!" But Mother's eyes twinkled. She snipped a thread from the last buttonhole and held out the coat. "Now I'll mark where the buttons go."

He put on the coat. "This is the last suit you'll have to make for me. By the time I outgrow this one I'll be taking care of myself."

"Maybe. But I made suits for Dudley after he was out of college. It takes quite a while for a lawyer to get started." Her eyes glowed. "But he's doing so well! Not just a successful lawyer—a respected lawyer. That's what someone said the other day. 'One of the most respected lawyers in New York City.' "

Cyrus thought of his brothers and squirmed. Jonathan and Matthew both well settled, Dudley a respected lawyer, Stephen leading his class at Williams, even little Henry starting to college at twelve. "I guess you're pretty disappointed in me. If I wanted to be a lawyer or a minister . . ."

She did not answer. She stepped back, head cocked, studying the coat. "That's it. Now take it off and I'll sew the buttons on."

From downstairs another "Mark my words, Dr. Field!"

Cyrus wiped his sweating hands on his shirt. If Mr. Holderby persuaded Father to change his mind . . .

That night after prayers Father pulled himself to his feet. "Cyrus, I'd like to talk with you."

His heart sinking, he followed his father into the little book-lined study and closed the door.

Father sat at his desk, his face sad, his eyes clouded. At last he spoke. "Son, you know I'd be happier if you wanted to enter a profession. But you don't. So . . ." The silence stretched. "Well, a man must do what he finds it in his heart to do." Another silence. "I don't know just how you'll make out in New York. If you decide it's a mistake, don't be ashamed to come home.

"Put me off in front of Stewart's—please."

In a few moments he was alone in the crowd on Broadway, staring at the biggest store he had ever seen. Slowly he walked toward the entrance; he passed it. I'll go around the block once, he decided, and then I'll . . . The fourth time around the block he said: The next time you've got to go in!

Somehow he found himself on Murray Street, walking west. I'll walk three blocks, he thought. Then I'll come back and march straight in that store. I'll . . . He saw a sign: Lodging. That's what I ought to do first! I ought to see about room and board near where I'll be working! He climbed the steps and knocked.

Room and board, the landlady told him, would be two dollars a week. Yes, she admitted two dollars a week was high. But prices were going up, and she prided herself on setting a good table.

When he left the house he had paid one week in advance, to begin next Monday. Now, he told himself, you've got to get a job!

"I want to see Mr. Stewart, please!"

Heads jerked; clerks and customers turned to stare at him. Confound it, what had made him shout?

The clerk, as though to reprove him, spoke very softly. "Your name, sir?"

"Cyrus Field."

The clerk smiled. "Oh! Any relation to David Dudley Field?"

"I'm his brother. But he's not—I mean I'm not—I'm getting a job on my own!"

After a wait that seemed forever he was in Mr. Stewart's office.

"So you're David Dudley Field's brother?"

"Yes, sir, but I'm getting my own job, myself."

"So? Sit down, my boy, and tell me what experience you've had."

Cyrus explained how he had kept the family accounts for three years—ever since he was twelve.

"I see. Do you know double-entry bookkeeping?"

"Uh—no, sir."

"Hmm. . . . Well, we can use another errand boy. How well do you know New York City?"

"I don't. I just got here this morning, Mr. Stewart."

Mr. Stewart's eyebrows went up. "And you're applying for a job the first thing?"

"No, sir. The first thing I got a room over on Murray Street."

Mr. Stewart's eyebrows stayed up. "You must have been quite sure you'd get a job here."

Cyrus hesitated, then blurted out, "No, sir. I was really stalling around, getting up the nerve to come in."

Mr. Stewart's eyes twinkled. "Cyrus, I believe you'll get along all right. I don't generally hire an errand boy who doesn't know the city, but I'm inclined to try you. Here's a map of New York. If you study it—"

"I'll learn it by heart!" He was going to get the job! Wouldn't Dudley be surprised when he strolled in and said, "Sorry I'm a little late, but I stopped to talk to Mr. Stewart." Wouldn't everybody—

"And even though you don't know the city," Mr. Stewart went on, "I'm going to start you at the usual salary for new errand boys. Fifty dollars."

Fifty dollars! His heart hammered. Of course, Mr. Stewart didn't mean fifty dollars a week—no boy could earn that much—but just to think of making fifty dollars a month!

"Do you want to start tomorrow, or wait till Monday?"

"I'll start tomorrow, sir!" As soon as he got his first month's pay he could send that eight dollars straight back to Father, and another eight besides. He could—

Mr. Stewart jotted something on a card. "Give this to the man at the door when you come in tomorrow morning. Our errand boys report at six-thirty and work until we close at night. But you'll get an hour off for dinner and forty-five minutes for supper, so it's really not much more than a twelve-hour day."

Cyrus took the card and got up grinning. "I'll be here bright and early, sir!" He could help Father out all the time with money for Stephen and Henry. He could—

"By next year," Mr. Stewart said, "if you turn out well—and I have a feeling you will—we'll raise you to a hundred. By the time you've been here three years, you'll probably be making a dollar a day."

"*A—dollar a day?*"

Mr. Stewart beamed. "Surprises you, eh? I've seen bright hard-working boys get ahead that fast; start at fifty dollars a year and work right up to a dollar a day in three years."

"Yes, sir. Thank you, sir." He managed to keep the smile on his face as he left Mr. Stewart's office. He even managed to smile all the way through the store until he reached the street.

Chapter 2

"Young Man in a Hurry"

AGAIN CYRUS WAS ALONE IN THE CROWD ON BROADWAY. Two hours ago he had been scared; now he was heartsick. His board and room over a hundred dollars a year, his salary fifty dollars—if he worked out all right.

I'd better start learning the city! he told himself.

Map in hand he wandered south, then east, trying to memorize the tangle of streets. He didn't remember how many times he got lost. When he reached Dudley's house that evening supper was over.

Dudley shook hands and slapped him on the back. "So you went right after a job? Good for you! Get washed up and eat; then come on in the library and tell me about it!"

He dawdled over his supper. He knew he was stalling, trying to put off the minute when he'd have to tell Dudley what a failure he was. At last he got up and went slowly toward the library.

Two strangers were talking with Dudley.

"So," the older man said, "going to be a lawyer like your brother, eh?"

"No, sir. I'm going into business." Cyrus tried to

sound brisk and confident. "I have a position with A. T. Stewart's."

"A position? Well, well! Clerk? Or bookkeeper?"

"Errand boy," Cyrus admitted. He sat down, suddenly so sleepy he had to fight to keep his eyes open, and waited for the visitors to leave. It seemed they would never stop talking.

They were asking Dudley's advice. Cyrus tried to follow the conversation, but the tangle of "whereas" and "wherefore" and "party of the first part" was worse than the tangle of New York streets. At last the visitors got up, said good night, and started toward the door.

The younger man paused. "Oh, did you hear about that electrical contraption Samuel Morse is working on? Calls it his 'magnetic telegraph.' Says he's going to send messages through wires. Any distance. New York to Washington, even! Instantly!"

The older man snorted. "Bah! I don't know what's the matter with Samuel Morse. Good blood in him. His brothers turned out all right. But that one! Why the son of a fine minister like Dr. Morse . . . What a disappointment that one must be to his family!"

Cyrus felt a hot flush crawling to his face. He shot a quick glance around, but nobody was paying any attention to him. I'd like to meet Samuel Morse, he thought. I'd tell him "I know just what you've been through!"

"Maybe Morse's telegraph is a crackbrained

scheme," the younger man said, "but what if it would work? Think what it would mean! Remember last December when one of our newspapers arranged to rush President Jackson's speech to New York? Used the fastest express service—I heard it cost them seven hundred dollars to do it—and it took fourteen hours and a half! Just think! If Morse could send messages instantly!"

The older man said, "Humph!"

They argued a while longer; at last they were gone.

Dudley said, "So you went right after your job and got it, eh?"

"Yes, sir, I—" Might as well tell it all and get it over with. "Errand boy. Fifty dollars a year. And my room and board—" He clenched his teeth to keep his chin from shaking. At last he managed to finish.

Dudley only nodded. "Of course you'll need a little help at first. I'll make up the difference between board bill and salary till you're earning your keep. How about other expenses? Can you handle them?"

"Oh, yes! Father gave me some money before I left home."

Dudley smiled. "Better spend part of it on shoe-blacking and a pair of brushes, hadn't you?"

Cyrus looked down at his shoes and flushed.

"Do you have a better suit?" Dudley asked.

"A brand-new one. The last thing before I left home—" He stopped again.

"Better wear it."

"I was saving it for Sunday."

"Maybe Mother can make you another one for Sunday. You'll need to look spick-and-span at Stewart's."

"Yes, sir."

Dudley studied him for a moment. "What's the matter, Cyrus?"

"I—I thought I'd be on my own. But I won't be earning enough to—"

Smiling, Dudley shook his head. "Young man in a hurry, aren't you? The important thing right now isn't what you'll earn; it's what you'll learn. It's this way, Cyrus—"

Another man came to see Dudley; another man shook hands with Cyrus and said, "So! Going to be a lawyer, eh?"

"No, sir. I'm going to be a businessman. I've got a —a job at Stewart's. Errand boy." He excused himself and went to his room.

Tired as he was he lay staring into the dark. How long would he be a nobody? Just the brother of David Dudley Field? The one who wasn't going to be a lawyer? All this year he'd have to depend on Dudley for half of his board bill. More than half. But he'd see that he didn't have to ask for anything else. With six whole dollars left of the eight Father had given him, he'd get along.

By mid-June he stared at his account book, appalled. Only fifty cents left! How had he spent five dollars and fifty cents in such a short time?

One pair shoebrushes	25 cents
One box shoe-blacking	12½ cents
Haircut	12½ cents
Turpentine (to get spots out of coat)	6¼ cents
Shoes mended	18¾ cents

On and on and on! Easy enough to see where the money went. It certainly cost a lot to live in New York and keep neat and well dressed.

For a long time he sat with his head on his hands. He was a big success, he was! Dudley helping with his room and board—Mother making his clothes. And everybody disappointed in him. He knew that. Especially Dudley. No matter what Dudley said Cyrus could feel what he wasn't saying. "Too bad Cyrus doesn't want to be a lawyer."

A drop of water hit the page and made a blot on "haircut." I'm just tired, he told himself. I'll be all right tomorrow.

All the next day he found himself fighting a lump in his throat and a hollow feeling in his stomach. He left the store at closing time that night dragging his heels.

Mr. Jackson, an elderly clerk, fell in step with him. "Had about enough of it?"

"Sir?"

"Wish you were home again, sleeping in your own

bed, eating your mother's cooking?"

The truth hit Cyrus in the midriff. He was homesick! Homesick and scared!

"What'd you be doing right now," Mr. Jackson asked, "if you were home?"

Cyrus hunted frantically for something to say—anything—to change the subject. "Oh, I'm all right. It's just the heat. Errand boys really have it easy. But a clerk—you must have your hands full all the time, don't you?"

"Do I! Why, just this morning . . ."

Cyrus walked five blocks out of his way, listening to Mr. Jackson's woes. Finally he said, "I'm sorry, but I'd better say good night."

"Eh? Oh, too bad. Hope we'll have a chance to talk again, Cyrus. You're a mighty interesting lad. Got a head on your shoulders. If there's ever anything I can do to help, just let me know."

You've helped already! Cyrus thought. He went back to the airless, sticky heat of his room. Instead of tossing, turning, trying to sleep, he lay thinking of Mr. Jackson and his problems.

All at once it was morning. He got up smiling. The next time I can't stand thinking, he told himself, I'll start somebody talking!

All through the sweltering morning he whistled on his errands. By afternoon the whistle died. Just dried up, he decided. Down on South Street he stopped in the shade of a store, took off his hat, and mopped his sweating face.

A clerk was standing in the doorway. He said nothing. He just stood. Cyrus got uneasy. At home it was all right to stop in the shade to cool off. Wasn't it all right in New York?

"I just stopped to cool off," he said.

The clerk glanced at him. "Eh? Help yourself."

A carriage drew up and a well-dressed young man got out and sauntered toward the entrance.

"I've been watching for you, Mr. Taylor!" the clerk said. He lowered his voice. "Mrs. You-Know-Who is here, and she won't deal with anybody but the boss."

Mr. Taylor laughed, winked at Cyrus as though to include him in the joke, and went into the shop.

"Does he *own* this store?" Cyrus asked.

"He certainly does!" the clerk said. "And not yet thirty! That young man's made his mark!" He followed his boss inside.

If Mr. Taylor can do it, Cyrus told himself, *I can, too. I'll have my own business before I'm thirty!* He looked about him at the rows of stores. "Some day," he whispered, "you'll have to move over, gentlemen! You'll have to make room for Cyrus W. Field."

For almost a week he didn't have to fight the lump in his throat and the hollow feeling in his stomach. Then they came back again. More and more often he hunted for someone to talk with. More and more often he said, "You really have a job on your hands, don't you?" and listened. Listening seemed to help more than anything else. At night, when he was alone, he tried to think of the future, when he'd get out of a carriage and walk into his own store. By August all he could think of was the heat. If only winter would come!

It came. In December a gale howled in and drove temperatures down to zero. By day Cyrus waded snowdrifts and shivered. At night he shivered, too. No matter what he piled on top of the covers the cold crept up through the thin, hard mattress. He tried not to think of home—of heating bricks on the hearth and wrapping them in pieces of blanket to warm his bed. But the lump in his throat was an ache that would not go away.

He was plodding back to his room one mid-December night when the bell on City Hall clanged. *Fire!* He looked toward the tower to see which way the watchman swung the lantern to guide the firemen. Southeast.

A yelling mob in their red shirts came tearing down the middle of the street dragging their fire engine. In a few moments the bell clanged again. Two more yelling fire companies passed.

When Cyrus reached the boardinghouse half a dozen men were in the parlor, crowded around the hearth.

"Come on in, Cyrus, and thaw out!" one called. They made room for him.

He had not been there long enough to get warm

when all the church bells in the city set up a frantic clamor. The boarders looked at one another.

"It's a bad one!"

Someone banged on the door and yelled, "Turn out! Turn out! We'll need every able-bodied man in the city!"

Cyrus picked up his coat again and followed the others to the street. On Broadway he stopped with a gasp, staring south. A red glare lighted the sky.

When they got to the fire twenty buildings were blazing.

"Move back!" a fire chief shouted. "We can't save those! We've got to keep the fire from spreading!"

The red-coated men dragged their engines back,

and tried to train streams of water on roofs just beginning to smolder. Faster and faster they pumped. When they stopped, exhausted, others took their places. Men in top hats and evening coats toiled by workmen in corduroys.

But it was hopeless. The streams of water froze in mid-air. Flames leaped the narrow streets. Sixty buildings blazed—a hundred.

Unless they stopped the fire the whole city was doomed. But how could they stop it? The firemen were helpless, the engines useless, the hose frozen and burst. The howling wind carried embers three blocks from buildings already ablaze.

Desperately they planned. If they could blow up buildings in the path of the fire—flatten them—make a fire check . . . But they must have gunpowder—kegs of it—from the Brooklyn Navy Yard. What chance did a boat have to cross that stormy water tonight? A boat pushed off. Men watched—waited—prayed—and gave up hope.

Three hundred buildings blazed—four hundred—five hundred. Long after hope was gone, the boat came from Brooklyn with gunpowder.

Men cheered; then the cheers died in their throats as they watched the sailors start ashore into the burning city with the kegs of gunpowder. Time and again an ember fell on a blanket-wrapped keg and smoldered. The sailor paused only long enough to knock it off and beat out the fire. He marched on, carrying salvation for the city on his shoulder—or his own death. Depending on whether or not he got rid of the keg before it exploded.

One dull boom after another. Walls toppled. The fire check worked. But seven hundred buildings lay in smoking ruins. Only the burning of Moscow had ever destroyed that much property in a single fire.

Cyrus wandered into the burned-out region a week later and did not know where he was—there were no landmarks—until he heard a man ask, "Did you save anything, Mr. Taylor?"

The young man "who had made a mark for himself" shook his head. "Nothing."

"But you were fully insured, of course?"

"That won't help. The insurance companies are ruined, too."

"Then you—"

"I'm wiped out."

"But—but what will you do?"

Mr. Taylor stared at the blackened ruins, shrugged, and straightened. "Charge it to profit and loss and start over."

Cyrus walked away slowly. *If Mr. Taylor can do it, I can, too.* That was what he had been saying to himself. It was one thing to have the dogged stick-to-itiveness to climb inch by inch up your mountain to success. But to have an avalanche of disaster sweep you from your goal—to be wiped out and have to begin over . . . He wondered. The next spring he was still wondering.

"Cyrus, Mr. Stewart wants to see you. Right away."

His heart lurched. Wasn't he working out all right? Was Mr. Stewart going to fire him? Was he . . .

But Mr. Stewart was smiling. "Cyrus, I've been hearing very good reports about you. Quite a few of the clerks—especially Mr. Jackson—tell me you have a head on your shoulders. They've recommended that we try you out as a clerk."

Cyrus didn't have a bit of trouble smiling when he left Mr. Stewart's office. The clerks were smiling at him, too.

Mr. Jackson shook hands. "Don't know how you found your feet so fast, my boy, but you've done it!"

It's being a preacher's son in Stockbridge, Cyrus thought, and learning to listen! But he didn't go into that.

All he knew was that the homesickness was gone, and New York was his city. By the fall of '36, just a year after the fire, bigger, finer buildings had sprung from the ruins. Cyrus felt as proud of them as though he had built every one of them by himself. You can't stop us New Yorkers! That was what he liked to say.

His city! How it was growing! Lots marked out—on maps—clear up to what men said would some day be

Seventy-second Street! Land! That was the thing! Men bragged of buying lots at one hundred dollars and selling them for two thousand. Here a man had made eighty thousand on a piece of property he had bought only three years ago; there a man had made two hundred thousand!

Cyrus listened and smiled. One of these days he'd be investing. One of these days he'd . . .

The spring of 1837 the bubble burst. He saw a disaster greater than the fire sweep the city. Panic. No blackened ruins. Fine buildings stood—with FOR SALE signs on them. Banks closed. Businesses failed. Month after month, one failure after another.

"It's worse than the fire!" Cyrus told Dudley. "That was awful, but we stopped it in two days. We made a fire check. But how can you stop a panic? What can a man depend on, Dudley?"

Dudley's square jaw looked a little squarer. "His energy and his integrity. His ability to come back fighting! The only man who leaves his mark on the world is a fighter! Do you understand?"

"Yes . . . sir."

But New York had lost its savor. It was no longer the city where a boy could dream big dreams. When Cyrus got a letter from his brother in Lee, Massachusetts, he thought long and hard.

At last he went to talk it over with Dudley. "Matthew wants me to work for him in his paper mill."

"Matthew with a paper mill," Dudley said. "An odd business for him. His real love is engineering."

"You mean I shouldn't go?" Cyrus asked.

"I didn't say that."

"He's offering me two hundred and fifty a year and my board and room and washing. That's more than I'm making here."

Dudley only said, "Well?"

"What do you think?"

"That's your problem." Dudley's smile took the sting out of his words. "Young men in a hurry have to learn to make their own decisions."

Chapter 3

"So You're a Paper Salesman!"

AT THE FIRST SIGHT—AND SMELL—OF THE PAPER MILL Cyrus wondered if he had made the right decision. He stared at a pile of dirty rags and wrinkled his nose.

"That's the raw material," Matthew said. He picked up a sheet of crisp white paper. "And this is the finished product. It's quite a process."

"It must be." Cyrus tried to sound enthusiastic. "What do you want me to do?"

"Eventually you're going to travel for us. Take care of our customers from Boston to Washington. But first I want you to get acquainted with every process. So you'll know the business from the ground up. I'm turning you over to Mr. Wade."

Mr. Wade rubbed his long chin, looked Cyrus up and down, and said with a half smile, "From the ground up, eh? Yes, sir, I'll take care of him."

That's how it happened that Cyrus was sorting rags when Mr. Holderby of Stockbridge visited the mill.

"Well, well! So you got enough of New York, did you, Cyrus? I told you that you'd get your fill of it, didn't I? Remember what I said?"

Cyrus clenched his teeth, then answered quietly, "Yes, Mr. Holderby. You said 'Mark my words.' "

"Exactly! And I was right, wasn't I? I hear Stephen graduated at the head of his class."

"Yes, Mr. Holderby."

"Going to read law with Dudley."

"Yes, Mr. Holderby."

"And little Henry will graduate when he's only sixteen."

"Yes, Mr. Holderby."

"Your father can be mighty proud of those two boys."

"Yes, Mr. Holderby."

"By and large, your father can be mighty proud of his sons—most of them."

"Yes, Mr. Holderby."

"Yes, sir, Cyrus! I told you so!" The pudgy little man strutted off.

Mr. Wade glared after him. "Why didn't you paste him one?"

Cyrus managed to smile. "He's not as big as I am." He turned back to sorting rags.

"That's enough of that," Mr. Wade said. "I'm supposed to show you all the processes. So you'll know what you're talking about when you travel for us." He shook his head. "Traveling! I feel sorry for you! I wouldn't ride on those railroad cars if they gave them to me! You know what's the matter with this country? It's speed-crazy! That's what!"

"I'm going to like traveling," Cyrus said. *And the farther away from Mr. Holderby the better!* he thought.

"Then you can have it!" Mr. Wade told him.

After Cyrus had been traveling for a year he admitted to himself—never to anyone else—that travel did have its grim and gritty side. Hot, dirty rides in the summer. Cold, dirty rides in the winter. Drab restaurants and greasy food. At night, a lonely hotel room, and his paper work to do. Not just orders to write up, but a running account for himself of everything he had learned about every customer. I'm not dealing in paper, he told himself. I'm dealing with people. I've got to know them and remember them!

Matthew smiled over new accounts that Cyrus brought in. "You're doing all right! I wish money weren't so scarce. That I could pay you more. But you know how it is."

Yes, Cyrus knew. By the end of 1839, two and a half years since the panic had begun, things looked more hopeless than ever. Sometimes he spent half an hour listening to a man's troubles before they got around to talking about an order. At night the notes he kept for himself took more and more time.

He was working one night in a hotel room in New

Haven when he glanced at his watch and jumped to his feet. Almost nine o'clock! Young Mr. Stone, a new customer, had invited him to a party, and he had promised to come for a while. What would the man think of a salesman who forgot a promise?

Joseph Stone met him at the door and waved aside his apologies. "I know you're busy! Did you get caught up with your work?"

"Not quite," Cyrus told him. "But I did want to come in for a little while, to meet your friends, to—" He stopped. "And there's the person I'd like to meet first! That girl in blue!"

Mr. Stone glanced over the crowd. "Which one? I see three girls in blue."

"The pretty one! The one that's talking to those two —no, there are three men now."

"You really think you want to meet her?" Mr. Stone shrugged. "Well, let's join the crowd. We'll make five men for her to talk to." He led the way to the girl in blue. "Mary, here's someone who wants to meet you," he growled. "Why, I don't know. I should have warned him that you're the worst flirt in Connecticut." Then he began to chuckle. "My sister, Mary, Mr. Field."

Her smile was wide and friendly. "I'm so glad you could come!"

And Cyrus, who could talk to difficult customers from Boston to Washington, looked down into her dancing eyes and said, "Uh."

"And if Mary will let go of your hand," Mr. Stone suggested, "I'll introduce—"

Cyrus joined in the laughter. He tried to collect his wits, to remember the names. That dapper fellow who kept twirling his mustache—Horace Martin, a lawyer from Guilford. The red-headed man—

"Field?" Mr. Martin-with-the-mustache asked. "Any relation to David Dudley Field?"

"He's my brother."

"Don't tell me! And you're a paper salesman!" He made *paper salesman* sound a little lower than *rag-picker*. "But I thought Dudley told me his younger brother was going to read law with him?"

"That's Stephen."

"Oh! Stephen Field! Head of his class at Williams! That's my alma mater. I was there when he— And he's your brother, too! And you're—"

"A paper salesman." Cyrus finished it for him.

Horace Martin looked him up and down. "But how in the world did you ever happen—"

Mary Stone said, "Oh, my goodness, Horace! You're not in the courtroom!" She tucked her hand under Cyrus's arm. "Come on, and I'll see that you meet everybody."

"If you're ever in Guilford," Mr. Martin said, "look me up. I might be able to throw a little business your way."

Cyrus couldn't resist it. "I doubt if I'll get to Guilford. My accounts in Boston, New York, Philadelphia,

Baltimore, and Washington keep me rather busy." He swaggered a bit as he strolled off with Mary. She giggled and he grinned down at her. "Maybe," he said, "some day I should skip a few New York appointments just to get to Guilford!"

She laughed with him. "You must have an interesting life—traveling all the time. But dangerous! Do you ride in those awful railroad cars?"

"Of course! It's the only way to get anywhere!"

"There are still some stagecoaches."

"Do you know how long it would take me to get from New York to Washington by stagecoach? A week! But on the railroad—if I make good connections—I go all the way from New York to Washington in about fourteen hours!"

She shivered. "That's too fast. The railroads scare me to death. I hope they never put the stagecoaches out of business." Then she added, "But it must be exciting."

When the party began to break up, Cyrus—who had dropped in for a few minutes—was still talking to Mary. "Next time I'm in New Haven," he suggested, "I hope I'll get to see you."

"You might," Mary said, "if I'm visiting in New Haven."

"Oh . . . you don't live . . . where do you live?"

"In Guilford." Her eyes danced. "In Horace Martin's little town."

Cyrus found himself hunting for words again.

"Odd," Matthew remarked a month later. "Two new accounts in the little town of Guilford, Connecticut."

"What's odd about it?" Cyrus asked. "Don't you like new accounts?"

Matthew gave him a long, quizzical look. "What's her name?"

"I don't know what you're talking about!" Cyrus declared. "Besides, both times I was in Guilford, I missed her. She was— What are you laughing at?" Then he began to laugh, too, and explained about Mary Stone.

"Good luck," Matthew said. "Just don't neglect the bigger cities, please."

The next time Cyrus stopped in Guilford the first person he saw was Mary Stone.

"Why, Mr. Field, how good to see you! I've thought about you so many times!"

And Cyrus, who had been holding very witty conversations with Mary—in his mind—said, "Uh—you have?"

"All the traveling you have to do! Every time I read about a wreck I think of you!"

"I think about you, too. When I hear of a wreck." Then he added, "Some other times, too."

Mr. Martin came out of a building. "Oh, here you are, Mary. I was just on my way over to ask you—how about tonight at seven?"

"I'm so sorry," Mary said, "but I've asked Mr. Field to supper. Joseph's written so much about him. Mother wants to meet him."

Mr. Martin gave Mary a stiff smile, Cyrus an icy glare, and strode away.

Mary's eyes were full of mischief. "It was *almost* true. I was *going* to ask you to supper. What in the world ever brought you to Guilford?"

What if he told her "You did!"? But he said, "Oh, I like little towns, where everybody knows everybody else, and—"

"I know. Cities are awful, aren't they? So full of strangers."

"I remember my first sight of New York." Cyrus tried to make it sound very funny, but Mary didn't laugh.

" 'Long, lean, red-headed, and lost looking,' " she repeated. "You poor darling! How far you've come in five years! Joseph says you're a wonderful salesman. Not like a salesman at all. That you're a friend. You just sit and listen. Then try to help a man. It must be wonderful to be that kind of salesman!"

When Cyrus got back to his hotel room that night he sat a long time staring at his papers before he started working. If only the panic would end. If only . . .

"Still a young man in a hurry, aren't you?" he muttered. "It'll be years before you can even think about getting married."

Matthew continued to smile over new accounts from Guilford and New Haven, but he only smiled. After all, Cyrus was getting new accounts in the cities, too. Matthew whistled over one new name. "Hmmm! The E. Root Company of New York has had that account for years! Cyrus, you must be quite a salesman!"

It was the fall of 1840 that Cyrus got a letter from Mr. Root asking him to stop the next time he happened to be in New York.

"So you're Cyrus Field!" Mr. Root seemed surprised. "How old are you?"

"Almost twenty-one, sir."

"Not yet twenty-one, and you're the man who's taken several accounts away from me! I hear you're prompt and dependable."

"I should hope so. I don't sell paper. I sell service. And service a man couldn't depend on wouldn't be very good service, would it?"

Mr. Root smiled. "I agree with your philosophy. I regret the results."

Cyrus grinned. "I don't have a patent on being prompt and dependable."

"No. What I wanted to talk to you about—I'll admit I expected to see an older man—I'm looking for a junior partner."

When Cyrus left Mr. Root he stood on the street smiling up at the buildings. His New York! He'd be back again! Not just a clerk, but a junior partner in a New York firm.

Not until he was half asleep that night did a thought strike him that wiped the smile from his face. "Big cities are awful." That was what Mary had said.

In Guilford, Mary took one look at him. "Cyrus! Something's—is something wrong?"

"I'm not sure."

"Do you want to talk about it?"

"Yes. That's why I'm here."

Mary stopped him before he was half through explaining. "A junior partner in a New York firm before you're twenty-one! That's wonderful! And I thought something was bothering you. That long face. You just did that to tease me, didn't you?"

"But you don't understand. I'd live in New York. When I got married my wife would live in New York. We couldn't even get a house at first. I've been looking. We'd have to live in a boardinghouse. Have you ever seen those boardinghouses? Long and narrow. Jammed up against each other. No windows excepting at the front and back. Dark. Gloomy. Hot as an oven in the summer. And besides, you said big cities are awful."

"Oh, Cyrus!" Mary hid her face in her hands. Her shoulders shook.

"Please, Mary! Please don't cry! There's nothing to cry about! I'll refuse it. I'll—"

"I'm not crying! I'm laughing. Darling Cyrus, that was the most hindside-before proposal I *ever* had!"

Just after his twenty-first birthday Cyrus took his

bride to a boardinghouse in New York. After the light and air of a little town he knew how dark and gloomy the place must seem.

"It won't be for long," he promised. "I'm looking for a house all the time!"

"But wouldn't it be awfully expensive?" Mary asked.

He threw back his shoulders. "Please remember, Mrs. Cyrus W. Field, that your husband is a junior partner of E. Root and Company!"

It was not quite four months later that E. Root and Company went into bankruptcy.

Numb with shock Cyrus walked out of the building and stared unseeing at the busy, hurrying people. Bankrupt. How could he ever tell Mary?

Chapter 4

"Sunday Father"

"BANKRUPT!" MARY WHISPERED. "JUST WHAT DOES IT mean?"

"That we've failed. We can't go on. We owe more money than we can ever pay."

She whitened. "Will they put you in jail?"

"No, dear. Our country doesn't throw men in debtors' prison. The court will appoint a receiver. He'll go over our books—see how much we have and how much we owe. If we have only ten thousand and owe fifty thousand, he'll order us to pay off our debts at twenty cents on the dollar. The slate will be wiped clean and we'll be wiped out."

"Then what will you do?"

Cyrus remembered the fire of '35, and a young man staring at blackened ruins. "Start over again."

"Maybe you could get a job with Mr. Stewart," Mary suggested.

"I'm going into the paper business for myself."

"How can you?"

"I believe my personal credit is good. In spite of

what happened to E. Root and Company. I can get started. Then, if I work long enough and hard enough, some day I'll be where I thought I was when I asked you to marry me."

She looked up quickly. "If you had known the company was going bankrupt, you wouldn't have asked me to marry you?"

"Of course not! You think I'd ask anyone to go through what—"

"Then I'm glad you didn't know," she said. "I married you 'for better or worse,' because, no matter what happened, I wanted to be with you. Please don't be sorry we're married, Cyrus! What if we do have hard times? What if we never are rich? What if—"

"But I *will* be rich! I've *got* to be rich!"

"Cyrus!" Mary gasped. "I never heard you say a thing like that before! Why do you have to have a lot of money?"

"How else can I pay off those debts in full? And I'm going to, Mary! Maybe the law will wipe the slate clean at twenty cents on the dollar. But some day, somehow, I'll pay back every cent that every man lost in the bankruptcy of that company!" He put his arm around her. "Please don't look so worried. I'll always take care of you."

"I know. But will you take care of yourself?"

"I'll be all right. But it's going to be awfully lonesome for you."

Cyrus opened his business in small quarters in Burling Slip. The dawn-to-midnight days began. Week in, week out, month in, month out.

Their little daughter was born. He never saw her except on Sunday. "Some day," he said, "I'll have time to enjoy her."

"Babies change so fast," Mary said. "I wish . . . but I understand."

Her brother Joseph became a partner with Cyrus.

"Maybe now," Mary said hopefully, "you'll have a little more time?"

But he didn't. He traveled more, getting new customers, and more business from old customers.

He managed to rent a house. "It's clear out in the country," he told Mary, "on East Seventeenth Street. Dudley thinks it's crazy to go clear out there. Will you mind living so far out?"

"I'll love it," she said. "Maybe you'll have time to enjoy it."

He did not see much of their home except on Sunday. Holidays, great occasions, and visiting celebrities came and went in New York. He worked.

One night, after a year and a half of the grind, he said, "I'm going to take the morning off tomorrow."

Mary jumped up to feel his head. "You're sick!"

"No, no. There's something special going on."

"It must be special if you'll stop for it!"

"A man named Samuel Morse is going to demonstrate what he calls his telegraph. He's going to send messages through a wire, under water. For two miles! All the way from Castle Garden to Governors Island."

Her eyes widened. "And you'll stop for that?"

"Yes. The first night I was in New York . . ." He told her about "that preacher's son and his crackbrained scheme." "He'd already been working on his telegraph for three years then. Just think, Mary! He's been slaving over that machine for ten years! And everybody calling him a fool. Now he's going to show the world that he was right. Somehow, I want to be there when he does it. Would you like to go with me?"

"Go with you when you take time off?" She laughed. "All the omnibuses on Broadway couldn't stop me!"

Traffic down Broadway was worse than usual the next morning. When they reached Castle Garden the crowd was leaving.

"Is the demonstration over?" Cyrus asked.

"Some demonstration!" a man sneered. "We hear that 'something went wrong with the wire.' If you ask me, the whole thing is a hoax!"

"Let's go in," Cyrus whispered. "I'd like to speak to him."

They made their way through the disappointed, muttering crowd. On the platform they saw a machine that looked as though it had been put together of castoffs from this and that.

A tall, haggard man with burning eyes was pleading

with a portly, prosperous-looking fellow. "But it *was* working! We were getting signals through the line! Then something happened to break the connection! Please don't judge my magnetic telegraph by this mere accident! It will work! It does work! The day will come–"

The other man shook his head. "Sorry, Mr. Morse, but I don't want to invest in your contraption." He shrugged off the pleading hand and strode away.

Cyrus turned. "Let's go, Mary."

"But you wanted to speak to him."

"There's nothing I could say that would help." They followed the last stragglers from the building.

It was hard for Cyrus to work that day; a haggard face kept coming between him and the page.

Mary must have had trouble forgetting, too. That night she said, "I wonder if Mr. Morse is married."

"I heard his wife died years ago."

"Maybe it was better," Mary said slowly. "Think how awful it would be for a wife to hear men call her husband a crackbrained dreamer. Maybe *he* can forget what they say. He believes in what he is doing. But his wife would just have to listen, and she wouldn't know how to stand up for him. Poor man, I wonder what he'll do now?"

Two years later they had the answer. Samuel Morse the crackbrained inventor was suddenly Morse the genius. The telegraph succeeded.

Cyrus beamed over the news, but Mary didn't smile.

"Twelve years of heartbreak," she said. "I wonder if it was worth it?"

"To hang onto a dream that long and see it come true? Of course it was! Too bad his wife didn't live to share his big hour with him!"

"Maybe she wouldn't have lived through the last twelve years," Mary said soberly. "Maybe she would have died of heartbreak."

"Aw, Mary, you don't know how a man would feel when he had stuck to his guns until he showed the world he was right!"

"And you don't know how a woman would feel if people laughed at her husband. Oh, Cyrus, I'm glad you're not a genius!"

He grinned. "Don't worry. Not a glimmer of genius in me. Just a paper salesman." Late as it was he went to his desk.

Mary watched him for a moment. "Sometimes I think debtors' prison would have been easier."

"*What!*"

"You are in a kind of prison, you know. Dawn to midnight. You only get out on Sunday."

"Some day . . ." he promised.

"Yes, dear."

The endless grind went on. In 1845—war with Mexico. Crowds jammed the piers to watch regiments embark. Cyrus worked. In 1848 the war ended. People declared a holiday and paraded. Cyrus worked. In 1849—gold in California. Thousands sailed on the great clipper ships, to get rich in a hurry. Cyrus worked.

Longer hours when he was home. More trips away from home. Even when trains were almost on schedule it seemed to him they took forever. One Saturday when a train missed connections he hired a sleigh and drove the rest of the way through a snowstorm. He got home Sunday morning, as the family was finishing breakfast.

He hugged and kissed the children—how little he saw of them! Gracie was seven, Alice was five, little Belle was two, and the baby, as Gracie said, "was brand-new." It seemed to him only yesterday that Gracie herself had been "brand-new."

After their first squeals of delight the children eyed his valise expectantly. He pretended not to notice; then opened it and brought out three dolls.

"Take them in by the fire," he said. "They've had a cold ride."

Mary smiled, shook her head, and sat with him while he ate. "Darling, what a crazy thing to do! If that sleigh had upset—"

He teased her. "Let's see you frown!"

From the next room they heard Gracie's voice. "Mothers and fathers are different. Mothers are always, but fathers are just on Sunday. Mothers are the ones for when you need them."

His cup clattered against the saucer. Shocked, he stared across the table at Mary. "Is that the way they feel about me? That I wouldn't be here if they needed me?"

"Little girls don't understand about business, dear. I try to explain—tell them you're doing it for them."

But I'm not doing it just for them, Cyrus had to admit. I'm doing it for myself! To pay off a debt I don't even owe in the eyes of the law!

Did he have a right to live this way and work this way? To let his children grow up thinking "Fathers are just on Sunday"? Or should he . . . How could a man know what was right? He rubbed his hand across his forehead.

"Cyrus," Mary pleaded, "you're wearing yourself out! You're too tired!"

"Nonsense. I'm strong as a mule. I was just thinking."

But one morning not long after he did not get up. The room wouldn't seem to hold still. Mary called the doctor.

"What the devil's going on?" Cyrus asked him.

"You are!" the doctor growled. "You've been going on too fast and too long!"

"I have felt a little under the weather," Cyrus admitted. "I've been thinking of dropping around to your office for a prescription."

"I've got a prescription for you—if you'll take it."

"Of course!" Cyrus agreed. "Three times a day after meals! It'd be easier, though, if I could take it all in one big dose. When I'm busy—"

"This prescription doesn't come in a bottle. It's rest. Utter and absolute rest."

"Rest!" Cyrus glared. "That's impossible! I can't—"

"So?" The doctor settled back in his chair and stared out from under his eyebrows. "Cyrus, you and Mary have one of the happiest homes I've ever known. I'd hate to see it broken up."

"What are you talking about? If you think anything could break up our home—"

"The 'death of beloved husband and father' has been known to break up a home."

It was Mary who finally spoke. "You've been taking care of us for a long time. Now I'm going to take care of you. I'm going to put my foot down."

Cyrus had to smile at that. "Let's see you frown and make it stick."

"I wouldn't even try to frown. But I am going to put my foot down!"

Before the week ended the children were with their aunt in New Haven. When the next packet boat sailed for England Mary and Cyrus were on board.

Their doctor came to see them off. "England's the place for you! That'll slow you down. Not London, though. Some sleepy little town. And Mary, remember! Keep your foot down!"

Her eyes sparkled. "Don't worry! I'll take care of him!"

Four hours out from port she was pleading with the ship's doctor. "You've got to *do* something! My husband is *dying!*"

"No, ma'am, he won't die. Just wish he could. Seasick."

"What can I do for him?"

"Nothing. I'll do anything that can be done. And you—if you don't want him to bite your head off—clear out and leave him alone till he gets over it."

"You mean—be cross with me? My husband never said a cross word to me in his life!"

"That so? Then please clear out. Be a shame to spoil a record like that."

After two days a limp, exhausted Cyrus was stretched in a deck chair. He stared wearily at the horizon, then grinned at Mary. "Now I know why doctors advise a sea voyage for 'utter and absolute rest.' That's the longest I've stayed flat on my back in my life."

"Poor Cyrus! I felt so helpless!"

"So did I."

When they got back five months later their doctor came to see them. "Ha! That did the trick! You're a new man! Complete rest! That's what you needed! Where'd you stay?"

"Let's see, Mary, where were we?" Cyrus began to

tick off the names on his fingers. "Manchester, York, Edinburgh, Glasgow, Belfast, Dublin, London, Paris, Geneva—"

"What? How the devil could you—"

Cyrus grinned. "Perfectly simple. You know the first word I learned in any language? *Faster!*"

"I give up!" The doctor jammed his hat on his head. "I thought maybe you'd learned your lesson. But you haven't!" He stamped out.

Mary smiled with Cyrus, then was serious. "You will slow down, won't you, dear?"

"Some day," he promised. "This won't be forever. You know that, don't you?"

"Yes, dear." But she sounded as though she had her doubts.

Back to the dawn-to-midnight grind again. Sometimes at night he leaned back in his chair and closed his eyes while Mary read him the news and his mail. From Stephen, practicing law in California; from Matthew—he'd turned to his real love, engineering, and was making a name for himself building bridges; from Henry, who'd made his mark both as a minister and a writer. All of them big successes. Especially Dudley. His fame was spreading beyond New York City, now. He'd been appointed head of a commission to codify the laws of the state.

Yes, Cyrus thought, his brothers were making their

marks. And he? He was a man in debt. But some day . . .

It was five years later that the children came to breakfast one weekday morning and stopped to stare.

"Father! This isn't Sunday!"

He laughed and hugged them all. "Every day can be Sunday now. Uncle Joseph is going to run the business. I've retired."

"What's 'retired'?" Fanny wanted to know. She was six, and a walking question mark.

"It's what elderly gentlemen do," Mary said, "after about fifty years of hard work."

The youngster studied her father. "Are you an elderly gentleman?"

"No," Mary said. "He's not thirty-five. He just did his fifty years of hard work faster than most men."

Cyrus grinned at Mary until she smiled, then said, "How about a long drive this afternoon and a picnic supper?"

Fanny threw herself in his arms. "Let's go right now!"

"I have some letters to write this morning."

"Couldn't you do them tomorrow?"

"These are very important letters. I want people to get them right away."

The president of a bank called a meeting of the directors. "Gentlemen, this is an important occasion. I might say an occasion without equal in the annals of this bank. You'll remember back in forty-one the firm of E. Root and Company went into bankruptcy. We held a note for fifteen hundred dollars. The legal obligation was settled quite a while ago. I have here a personal check from Cyrus W. Field for over a thousand dollars. Thc balance, with interest at seven per cent, for a debt he did not owe in the eyes of the law. I think we should go on record with resolutions to show our appreciation of a man who . . ."

In a bare New England kitchen a lonely old woman sat down to a frugal supper. A huge cat licked his bowl, then rubbed against her ankles with a plaintive yowl.

The old woman sighed. "Thomas, I wish you were still young enough to forage for your own supper. You're old and useless. Do you know that? And so am I."

When someone knocked she started to the door, then turned back to set her plate on the mantel.

Someone knocked again and called, "Mrs. Alton?"

Oh, dear, it was Mr. Reed from the bank! What was wrong? Banks always frightened her. She tried to steady her shaking hands as she opened the door. "Do come in, Mr. Reed."

"I can't stop, ma'am. Some errands to run. Happy errands. You remember when your husband died and I helped you settle his affairs?"

"Yes. There was so little. You explained it—something about men couldn't pay what they owed. I didn't understand too well."

"Here's a check for you. Mr. Field didn't know where to reach you, so he sent it to me."

"But—but I thought the whole matter was over and done with?"

"So did I. Legally it's dead and buried. But Cyrus Field—" He backed away hastily when he saw her lips begin to tremble. He tried to make a joke. "I guess you might say Cyrus Field wouldn't let sleeping dogs lie, eh?" He hurried off.

She bit her lips, blinked, then straightened. She marched to the kitchen, took her plate from the mantel, and scraped the food into Thomas's bowl.

"There! Eat it all! I'm going shopping!"

The children loved their fine new home on Gramercy Park, clear out at Twenty-first Street. They loved having Uncle Dudley and nice old Mr. Peter Cooper for neighbors. Best of all they loved having a father for more than Sunday.

Of course sometimes at breakfast he'd say, "I think I'll drop in on Joseph a while this morning." And he would not come back until dark.

But they didn't scold him too often. They even made a joke about it and called him Sunday-and-Sometimes Father. At least they almost always had their evenings together.

Then one wintry night their Uncle Matthew came to supper. "Cyrus, there's an investment I think will interest you. This Mr. Gisborne—"

The children raised a storm of protests:

"No! He spends enough time with Uncle Joseph!"

"In a business he's retired from!"

"Not any more business!"

"But this wouldn't take his time," Uncle Matthew explained. "It's just an investment." He looked at Cyrus. "I halfway promised Mr. Gisborne that you'd talk to him tonight."

"See!" one of the youngsters wailed. "It *does* take time! Tonight we were going to finish *Pickwick Papers!* And you want him to talk business!"

Cyrus gave them a mock-ferocious glare. "Silence!" They giggled and subsided. "What sort of business is it, Matt?"

"Laying a submarine cable across the Gulf of St. Lawrence. Something about speeding up communication between England and America."

"Oh, dear," Mary said, "if it's anything about doing things *faster* . . ."

Cyrus laughed and went for his coat. "I doubt if I'll be interested. And even if I am, don't worry, Mary. It wouldn't take any of my time. Just be an investment. I'm no engineer or electrician, you know. There's no way I *could* spend time on a cable!"

Chapter 5

A Long Look at a Globe

"IF I HAD A GLOBE," MR. GISBORNE SAID, "I COULD SHOW you more clearly. But look at this map of the North Atlantic. Here is New York. Here—a good thousand miles northeast of it—is St. John's, Newfoundland."

Cyrus rumpled his hair. "Interesting. I never realized before how far Nova Scotia and Newfoundland do jut out into the Atlantic."

"Exactly. From Ireland to St. John's, Newfoundland, is just about half as far as from London to New York. Steamships take an average of two weeks for that London-New York voyage. But fast mail steamers could run from Ireland to St. John's in five or six days."

"And what's your idea?" Cyrus asked.

"To make it possible for America and Europe to get messages back and forth in six days instead of two weeks. To do that, we need to build telegraph lines across Newfoundland from St. John's to the western coast, and to lay a submarine cable across the Gulf of St. Lawrence."

"You think a submarine cable is practical?" Cyrus

asked. "I remember back in forty-two when Samuel Morse—"

"That was twelve years ago, Mr. Field. We've made progress since then. I laid a submarine cable myself from New Brunswick to Prince Edward Island."

"Quite a bit farther, isn't it, across the Gulf of St. Lawrence?"

"But the principle is the same! A longer cable, a bigger ship to carry it, and stronger paying-out gear to handle it! That's all!" Then he added grimly, "That and the cost. That's the problem."

"What have you done about it so far?" Cyrus asked.

"*What have I done about it? I've sweat blood! I've ruined myself! I've—*" Mr. Gisborne stopped. "I'm sorry. I didn't mean to get excited. But the last three years . . . It was just three years ago that I went to Newfoundland and put the idea before their legislature. They believed in my plan. They even made me a grant of five hundred pounds for a preliminary survey."

"Twenty-five hundred dollars—just to make a survey?"

"Yes, Mr. Field." Mr. Gisborne was grim. "A survey through four hundred miles of unexplored wilderness. Through land so wild we had to use a compass to find our way. It took me three months. I started with six white men. They gave up. I hired four Indians. Two of them deserted. The other two finished the survey with me."

"So out of ten picked men just two came through with you?"

Mr. Gisborne smiled wryly. "Doesn't say much for my choice of helpers, does it?"

"It says quite a bit about your endurance!"

For a moment Mr. Gisborne sat biting his lips as though fighting for control. "Thanks. I haven't heard very many compliments in the last few months. Well—to go on. I reported to Newfoundland. They gave me a charter, granting me the exclusive right to build telegraph lines in Newfoundland for thirty years. I came to New York. I got capitalists back of me."

"I shouldn't think it would be hard to raise money for telegraph lines."

"No? I'd built just forty miles of that Newfoundland line when my backers backed out. Dishonored my bills. Left me stranded. Disgraced. Owing fifty thousand dollars. The poor workmen on the job suffered most." He sat staring at the floor. "I gave up a good job in Nova Scotia to go to Newfoundland. Superintendent of Nova Scotia's telegraph lines. Of course my friends and relatives thought I was a fool. I could face that. But when my backers deserted me I was worse than a fool. I was a villain who had robbed the poor." He clenched his fist. "But it can be done, and it's worth doing! Europe already has over forty thousand miles of telegraph lines, and they are building more every day. Almost the whole continent can get messages as far as Ireland in a matter of minutes—even seconds. North America has over thirty thousand miles of telegraph lines. We can communicate from Halifax, Nova Scotia, to New Orleans in a matter of minutes. You know how much quick communication means in the United States, don't you?"

"Oh, yes!" Cyrus agreed. "No doubt about that."

"But it still takes two weeks to get messages from London to New York by steamer. If we can extend the North American lines to St. John's, Newfoundland, and use fast mail steamers from Newfoundland to Ireland, we can cut the communication time between America and Europe to five or six days instead of two weeks. Can't you see what it would mean?" He talked on and on.

"You say you had built forty miles of the land line across Newfoundland, and are fifty thousand dollars in debt?" Cyrus asked. "How long would that land line be?"

"Four hundred miles."

"But good heavens, man! At that rate it would cost half a million dollars! How could you spend half a million just putting up poles and stringing wires along a road—"

"There aren't any roads. We have to build that road as we go. An eight-foot road, hewn out of the wilderness."

"I'm sorry, Mr. Gisborne," Cyrus said, "but I don't

have that kind of money to invest."

"But you know men who do have money! If you'd interest them—"

"I'll think about it," Cyrus promised. "I'll give you a definite answer in—will three weeks be soon enough?"

"Yes, Mr. Field." Mr. Gisborne's shoulders sagged. "I've waited longer than that for answers."

Poor devil, Cyrus thought, he knows I'm not really interested. "I will think about it," he said again.

"Yes, Mr. Field. Thank you very much for listening."

All the way home Cyrus tried to fight off the feeling that he was a scrounge. He found Dudley in the library talking with Mary. "Sorry I'm late. It took a little longer than I thought it would."

"What did he want?" Mary asked.

He spun the globe to the North Atlantic and explained Gisborne's idea.

"More than half a million to build a line across Newfoundland?" Dudley shook his head. "A pretty heavy investment that might—or might not—pay off."

"I know. I'm not thinking of going into it. But Gisborne—remember that day at Castle Garden, Mary? And Samuel Morse pleading for someone to believe in him? Gisborne reminded me of Morse. Worn to a frazzle but holding on like grim death to his idea."

Dudley nodded. "I know. It's hard to forget a chap like that. Poor devils. You never know whether they're fools or geniuses."

"Gisborne knows his telegraphy," Cyrus declared. "He wouldn't have been superintendent of the Nova Scotia telegraph lines if he didn't." Mary's eyes were anxious. "Don't worry," he said. "I'm not thinking of investing. All the money I could invest wouldn't be half what he'll need. And I've worked hard enough long enough. I'm ready to slow down and enjoy myself."

Dudley laughed. "Ready to enjoy yourself maybe."

Dudley said good night. Mary went to see about the children. Alone in the library Cyrus turned to the globe again. How far Newfoundland jutted out into the Atlantic! With a submarine cable to bridge the Gulf of St. Lawrence—of course it would be longer than the other cable Mr. Gisborne had laid, but as he said the principle was the same. A longer cable, a bigger ship to pay it out . . . Then a thought sent a prickle up his spine. If a cable across the St. Lawrence was possible what about a cable across the Atlantic?

When Mary returned Cyrus was at his desk writing furiously. He paused a moment. "Mary! What if we could lay a cable across the Atlantic? And have news from Europe in two minutes instead of two weeks! Not just cutting the time a bit! Annihilating time!"

"A cable clear across the ocean? Oh, Cyrus, that sounds utterly impossible."

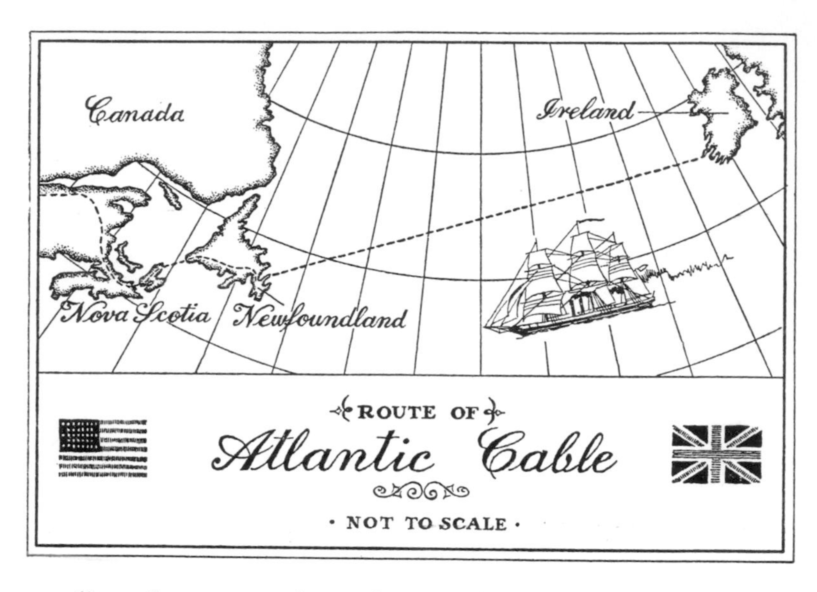

"Maybe it is, and maybe it isn't. One thing sure, I'm going to find out."

"How?"

"I'm writing to Samuel Morse and to Matthew Fontaine Maury."

"Maury? Who's he?"

"Superintendent of the National Observatory in Washington." He grinned. "Another man like Morse—that everybody called a fool until he proved he was a genius. He made the charts that have cut the sailing time of sea voyages in half. It used to take six months to sail from New York to San Francisco around the Horn. Now some of our clippers have done it in ninety days."

"Oh," Mary said. "Maury found a way to do things

faster. No wonder you know about him."

He smiled with her. "Maury's had expeditions out sounding the North Atlantic, too. He'll know whether or not we can lay a cable on the bottom of the ocean. And Morse will know whether or not we can signal through the cable after we get it laid."

"But Cyrus . . ." He did not answer. His pen raced over the paper again. She sighed and bent to kiss him. "Good night, dear."

He started and glanced up. "Mary! Don't look so solemn! I won't get into this unless they say it's practical. And even if I do get into it, it wouldn't take much of my time. I wouldn't be building the lines or laying the cable, you know. Just getting the backing for it."

When he had finished his letters he was too excited to sleep. Cold as it was he went out to walk. If only Peter Cooper were awake—but Mr. Cooper's house was dark. Maybe Dudley—yes, a light still burned in Dudley's library.

"A cable clear across the Atlantic!" Dudley stared. "Have you the faintest idea what it would cost?"

"Not the slightest," Cyrus admitted. "But when we're ready to lay it, I'll raise the money to do it. Meanwhile—the Newfoundland line. That's the thing now. If I can get ten men to go in with me—each of us put up a hundred thousand—we can build that line in jig time."

"How many men do you think would invest a hundred thousand in telegraph lines in that wilderness?"

"I'll talk to Mr. Cooper first."

"Not a chance," Dudley said. "He's all wrapped up in his Cooper Union. He's pouring all his time and money into it. That's his big dream, Cyrus."

"An Atlantic cable is a bigger dream. When I talk to him . . . I wish it weren't so late. But tomorrow the first thing I'll—"

"Before you've heard from Morse or Maury?"

"Why wait for that?" Cyrus asked. "When I hear from them I'll have the backers all lined up and be ready to get to work on that Newfoundland line."

Dudley smiled. "Still a young man in a hurry, aren't you?"

"But we need to be in a hurry about this. Summers are short in Newfoundland. We won't have a very long season to work. If we want to get those lines laid before winter we'll need—"

"Cyrus! It's after midnight! Clear out!"

"But there are so many things to settle before—"

"Then settle them with your scientists! I'm a lawyer! Good night!" Dudley pointed to the door.

"But we'll need a lawyer. For instance—a new charter from Newfoundland. We'll have to have a clause to protect our investment. The exclusive right to land ocean cables on Newfoundland for a certain number of years."

"Good night, Cyrus! And . . . Hmmm . . . Yes." Dudley turned to his desk. "Let me see: Whereas: . . ."

It was after one o'clock when he said, "Then there's the matter of supplies. You'll need to be able to land them duty free. And . . ." It was after two o'clock when he stopped making notes. "Well, Cyrus, if your plan goes through you'll have a lawyer to help you. But I have my doubts. You won't get men to listen ten minutes to—"

"You've listened for three hours." Cyrus got up. "Tomorrow I'll see if Peter Cooper will listen."

"So," Mr. Cooper said, "Mr. Gisborne's company failed after only forty miles of line were built? That's not much of a recommendation, is it, Cyrus?"

"It didn't fail from an engineering point of view. Just the money—"

"If Gisborne, a respected engineer, can't interest capital—"

"But Gisborne wasn't talking about an Atlantic cable! I am! I'll not stop till I've linked the old world and the new!"

Peter Cooper's eyes began to dream. "Linked the old world and the new. It could mean a lot. A lot to the peace of the world. The war of Eighteen-Twelve would never have been fought if we could have gotten messages back and forth more quickly. The price of one week of war—one day—would pay for a cable. A link between . . ."

Cyrus held his breath and waited.

At last Mr. Cooper said, "Yes, Cyrus, it is worth doing. If Mr. Morse and Mr. Maury say it's practical, and if you can get ten backers for your Newfoundland line, I'll be one of them. I won't have much time to devote to it—"

"Don't worry about that!" Cyrus told him cheerfully. "Any running around, letter writing, things like that—I'll take care of."

"How will Mary and the children feel if you get tied up—"

"Oh, this won't take too long. If we get right after it we can take care of Newfoundland this summer and lay the Atlantic cable next summer. And by the time I hear from Morse and Maury I'll be ready to go!"

"You think you'll have your ten backers by then?"

"Ten? I'll probably have twenty!"

Cyrus had no trouble getting appointments to talk with financiers. Any businessman was ready to listen to him. After all, hadn't he started his career up to his ears in debt, and made his fortune before he was thirty-five?

At last he had five backers. Half the number he needed. And there the number stuck. At home the children looked at him wistfully. Was he going to be a Sunday Father again?

"This is the only part that will take my time," he explained. "Just to get the ball rolling. When I have five more backers . . ."

But that was the problem. Some men laughed at the idea of an Atlantic cable; some said it might work but they preferred a safer investment. Some men were bitter against England. Again and again, when a man's face hardened and his lips tightened, Cyrus knew he was going to hear another tirade against England:

"A cable to England? Hah! They already think they rule the waves! Why help them rule the bottom of the sea, too?"

"A cable to England? No, thanks! George Washington advised us against foreign entanglements. And he was right! The farther we stay from England the better!"

"England! Hah! You're too young to remember what happened in the war of Eighteen-Twelve. When the redcoats burned Washington! Well, some of us do remember it! I wouldn't spend a dollar on a cable between us and England!"

"Cyrus," Mary asked one day, "shouldn't you wait till you hear from Mr. Morse and Mr. Maury? Till you know whether or not—I mean what if the idea is just a—a crackbrained scheme?"

"I can't wait, Mary. When their answers come we must be ready to move!"

Mr. Morse's answer came first. Cyrus read the letter and looked up beaming. "He says it's perfectly practical—I mean *practicable*. He gives me quite a lecture on the difference. I must remember that. And this—just listen to this! It's amazing! Morse says he predicted an Atlantic cable in forty-three." He shook his head. "And here I thought I had hold of a brand-new idea."

"In forty-three," Mary said. "Before his land line worked. When people were jeering and calling him a crackbrained dreamer."

Cyrus looked at her quickly. Had she heard the remarks that were going around about one Cyrus W. Field? Surely not. No one would say things like that in front of a man's wife!

Mr. Maury's answer came. Cyrus started to read, then looked up. "Well, I'll be . . . When Maury got my letter he had just finished writing a letter to the Secretary of the Navy on that very subject! An Atlantic cable! He's sent me a copy of it. Listen to this:

"From Newfoundland to Ireland, a distance at the nearest points is about sixteen hundred miles, and the bottom of the sea between the two places is a plateau, which seems to have been placed there especially for the purpose of holding the wires of a submarine telegraph and keeping them out of harm's way . . ."

He read other bits of Maury's letter to Mary, but there was one part that he skipped:

Nor do I pretend to consider the question of finding a time calm enough, a sea smooth enough, a wire long enough, a ship big enough . . .

No use worrying her with that. They'd solve those

problems when they came to them. Now, with these answers, he'd get five more backers in a hurry!

For the next two days he talked so many hours that he wondered if he talked in his sleep, too. Not another backer. The second night he came home gray-tired.

"Mr. Cooper wants to see you, Cyrus," Mary said. "No matter what time it is when you come in, he said."

He flinched. How long had it been since he had told Mr. Cooper he'd get ten backers—even twenty? In spite of the cold his hands were sweating when he knocked on Mr. Cooper's door.

"Just five backers, eh?" Mr. Cooper asked. "Moses Taylor, Clifford White, Marshall Roberts, and you and me. Well, why bother?"

"But I will get the other five!" Cyrus pleaded. "I'll get them! Just a few more days and—"

"Why bother with them? I think the five of us can swing that Newfoundland line."

"You mean—"

"Talk to the others. Tell them I'm ready to put up one-fifth of the cost. I think they'll agree to do the same."

Home again Cyrus gave Mary a hug that swung her off her feet. "We'll do it!"

"Has Mr. Cooper found the other backers?"

"No, but he says if the five of us double our investment—each puts up two hundred thousand—"

"Oh, Cyrus!"

"I'll have to sell stocks that are paying dividends, to invest in something that won't pay dividends till the Atlantic cable is laid. We'll be a little scrimped for a while."

"We've been there before. I'm not thinking about the money. It's you. You've been working harder over this than you ever did in business. You've looked so—so driven."

"Getting the backing has been a bit of a job," he said. "Harder than I thought it would be. But after we're organized I'll turn things over to the engineers and electricians. We'll have a meeting or so with Mr. Gisborne to get the picture. That's all."

Mr. Gisborne's eyes lighted when he saw Cyrus. "You've been thinking about it?"

"Thinking? I've been doing! I have a group ready to form a company and build that Newfoundland line if they can get the charter they want from Newfoundland."

"No question about that," Mr. Gisborne said, "they gave me very generous terms."

"We'll want more than that. For one thing we'll want the exclusive right to land ocean cables on Newfoundland for fifty years. Especially an Atlantic cable."

Mr. Gisborne's head jerked up. "Whatever gave you that idea?"

"Studying the globe. Frankly, your idea didn't interest me too much—merely cutting a few days off the time of communication between Europe and America. But an Atlantic cable—to annihilate time—that's something else again!"

"I wonder," Mr. Gisborne said slowly, "if I'd have been better off if I'd told my backers my whole idea. That the Newfoundland line was just the beginning. The first step toward an Atlantic cable."

"You thought of it, too?"

"Of course."

Cyrus jumped to his feet impatiently. "Then why didn't you say so?"

"Maybe I should have. But I corresponded with John Brett about it. He's one of the best cable men in England. He estimated it would cost almost four million dollars to lay an Atlantic cable. And the obstacles are terrific. A cable to span more than sixteen hundred nautical miles of ocean, most of it more than two miles deep—"

"We'll cross the Atlantic when we come to it! Right now, the question is the Newfoundland line. Can you be at my house this evening? If we can spend a few hours getting the picture—"

"We'll probably spend more than a few hours," Mr. Gisborne said.

Night after night men gathered in the library with

Mr. Gisborne, going over the facts and figures. Mr. Gisborne didn't mince words when he laid the problems before them. The backers didn't mince matters when they made their plans. They had already agreed to invest a million dollars in the Newfoundland line. Now they accepted the fact that it might cost a million and a half. They would disband the old company, pay off the fifty thousand in debts, and hire Mr. Gisborne to build the Newfoundland line—if the government of Newfoundland would give them the charter they wanted.

"I'll have to go to Newfoundland," Cyrus told Mary, "about that charter. The four of us—Dudley, Mr. Gisborne, Mr. White, and I—"

"By boat?" she asked.

He flushed. "Of course. It's the only way."

"Oh, Cyrus! You poor dear! I hope you've outgrown seasickness!"

He hadn't. A few hours out from the port he was in his bunk.

"Good Lord, Cyrus!" Dudley said. "I had no idea you got this sick! If I had— But I guess you'd have had to come, anyhow."

The ship's doctor sympathized, too. "This has been one of the roughest trips I've ever made," he said. "In the dining room I have to hold on to the table with one hand and try to eat with the other."

"At least I'm not having that trouble," Cyrus muttered.

"Wish I could help. Doesn't seem to be much to do for you. Just keep quiet. Try not to worry. Hereafter, stay off the North Atlantic. Roughest ocean in the world. Did you know that? I saw some data by a fellow named Maury once."

All the way to Newfoundland the ship pitched and rolled, and Cyrus thought of Maury's letter. For the first time he began to wonder.

Nonsense, he told himself. It's just because I feel so rotten.

But the words still pounded through his head: *A time calm enough, a sea smooth enough.*

Chapter 6

"Yes, Mr. Field! Quite a Problem!"

IN ST. JOHN'S, AS CYRUS AND MR. GISBORNE LEFT THE boat together, a burly fellow blocked their way and glared at the electrician. "What are you doing back here?"

Mr. Gisborne flushed, but answered quietly, "I've come back to finish the job I started. To build a telegraph line across Newfoundland."

"You and who else? Think there's a man in Newfoundland you can trick into working for you again? Mighty fine promises you made! We left our nets and boats. We sweated and slaved for you. Then you walked out and left us without a penny of pay."

"It wasn't Mr. Gisborne's fault!" Cyrus said. "Don't you know that? His backers welshed on their promises to him. He—"

"I don't know anything about backers. All I know is that *he* made promises and *he* didn't pay."

"Well, now he's got backers who won't back out," Cyrus declared. "We're going to build that line!"

"Ha! Can't build a telegraph line with backers. You need workers! And you won't get any around here!"

"The first thing we're going to do is to pay off every cent that's owed to every man in Newfoundland. You and every other man who worked on the line will get every penny coming to you."

"Ha! That I want to see!"

The legislators weren't quite so outspoken as the workman, but they were hard to convince. Arguments flew thick and fast. What if another company backed down and failed as the first one had done?

"Do you think men are going to spend fifty thousand to clear up old debts," Cyrus asked, "unless they intend to carry through?"

They got the charter they asked for; a St. John's paper carried the news: The New York, Newfoundland and London Telegraph Company was ready to pay off all debts of the former telegraph company. If all persons with bills to present . . .

At first a mob stormed the door. But after ten, then twenty, then fifty men walked out paid in full, the crowd subsided and waited in line. They even joked back and forth:

"A cable across the Atlantic! Aren't they the ones!"

"Balmiest idea I ever did hear! They'll never do it!"

"Crazy. But honest. I'll say that for them. Spending ten thousand pounds to pay debts that's none of their concern."

"And planning to spend three hundred thousand pounds in Newfoundland!"

"Just getting ready for that cable they'll never lay!"

"Poor blokes."

"Ah, what's money to them? Money grows on trees in America!"

Dudley looked at Cyrus, but said nothing. He didn't need to say anything. Mr. Gisborne was silent, too.

It was Mr. White who changed the subject of what they weren't talking about. "If we're going to try to keep six hundred men on the job we'll need our own ship to transport supplies. I've heard there's a vessel in Halifax we might get. I wish I could stop on our way back to New York, but—" He looked at Cyrus.

"I'll do it," Cyrus promised. "After all I'm the man with time on my hands. Joseph Stone will appreciate this telegraph company. It'll keep me out from under his feet."

Not two months later Joseph Stone died.

After the first shock of her grief over the death of her brother Mary asked, "What will you do, Cyrus? Sell the business?"

"Not just now," he said. "I'll take over and run it again myself."

"But how can you manage that, and take care of things for the telegraph company, too?"

"It shouldn't be too long before the land line across Newfoundland is done," he said. "Not with six hundred men on the job."

And he wrote to Matthew, who was working with Mr. Gisborne, building bridges for the road across Newfoundland. How many months did he think the land line was going to take?

Matthew's answer came:

How many months? Let's say how many *years!* Recently, in building half a mile of road we had to bridge three ravines. Why didn't we go around the ravines? Because Mr. Gisborne had explored twenty miles in both directions and found more ravines. That's why! You have no idea of the problem we face. We hope to finish the land line in '55, but I wouldn't bet on it before '56, if I were you!

Cyrus paced the floor in Dudley's library. "Another year before the land line is done! It'll be fifty-six before we're ready to lay the St. Lawrence cable, and fifty-seven before we're ready to lay the Atlantic one. Unless— I have it! Why don't we work on both ends at the same time? Lay the St. Lawrence cable now, while they're building the land line! That's it!"

He made an appointment to talk it over with Mr. Morse. Yes, Mr. Morse agreed, that would be practicable. Of course it was too late to lay the St. Lawrence cable this year.

"Why too late?" Cyrus asked. "If we order the cable from England immediately—"

"It will take time for them to make it for you."

"To make it? You mean they don't have cable ready to sell?"

"No, Mr. Field. You'll have to order the cable and have it made. And before they can make it they'll have to know the conditions where you are going to lay it. If someone would go to England and talk to John Brett . . ."

Cyrus booked his passage to England in January of '55. What was it he had said just a year ago? "No way I could spend time on a cable." But now, when someone should see John Brett, he was the someone.

Cyrus liked John Brett on sight. A foursquare sort of man. Sturdily built, square-faced, with deep-set eyes. A quiet man, whose voice was a pleasant rumble.

At the mention of an Atlantic cable John Brett merely nodded. "Hmmm . . . Yes. I wonder how many men have dreamed of that."

"The idea struck me all of a heap," Cyrus said. "I thought I'd hit on something new. But I found that Samuel Morse and Matthew Fontaine Maury had both been thinking about it."

"Of course, Mr. Field. Any man interested in electricity or the ocean couldn't help thinking about an Atlantic cable. There's been talk about it over here for years. Frederick Gisborne and I carried on quite a correspondence about it. Professor Thomson at the University of Glasgow talked of it. Charles Bright, the chief engineer of our Magnetic Telegraph Company, stood right up in public and predicted it." He smiled.

"And got laughed at. If Englishmen would listen to any man it would be Charles Bright. He's one of the most practical and experienced telegraph engineers in England. But when he predicted an Atlantic cable the kindest thing said was that he was 'a very sanguine young man.' "

"So there is talk about an Atlantic cable over here?" Cyrus asked. "Good!"

"Yes, talk about it. For it and against it. Mostly against it."

"But if the scientists believe in it—"

"Not all of them," John Brett said. "And it's one thing to predict a cable and something else to make that prediction come true. It will take manufacturing know-how to make it, engineering know-how to lay it, and money—you have no idea how much money—to finance it."

"I'm no engineer," Cyrus remarked, "but I've raised better than a million dollars to finance the New York, Newfoundland and London Telegraph Company."

"Capital here and in America?" Mr. Brett asked.

"All in America."

"Then I'd like to represent the first British capital. May I invest five thousand pounds in the New York, Newfoundland and London Telegraph Company?"

"I wish," Cyrus told him, "that all stock was that easy to sell!"

"And just now," Mr. Brett said, "your problem is a

submarine cable across the Gulf of St. Lawrence."

Cyrus nodded. "And they tell me you're the man to talk to."

"Yes. Just the man." For some reason Mr. Brett looked amused.

"I've heard of your success in laying cables."

"I have more to recommend me than that, Mr. Field. Some failures, too. That's quite a recommendation. I've learned so many things *not* to do. You see, submarine cable is in its infancy. We have to do a great many things wrong before we learn to do them right."

"I never thought of that."

"From time to time you will. For instance," Mr. Brett said, "when I laid the first Dover-Calais line it failed. Too light. The ocean currents dragged it back and forth. The rocks cut it. So I learned one lesson. Cable had to be heavier."

"The heavier the better, eh?" Cyrus asked. "I'll remember that."

"That's what I thought," Mr. Brett said. " 'The heavier the better.' When I started to lay a Mediterranean line I ordered a whale of a cable. Eight tons to the mile. We started paying it out. We got over an uncharted deep spot. The cable ran faster and faster. Nothing we could do to hold it back. It jumped the groove of the paying-out gear and sliced through a bulwark. Luckily we got past that deep spot. The cable slowed down of its own accord. We began to breathe again. I'll tell you for a while we thought it would cut the ship in two! So I learned something else. A cable can be too light for shallow water; it can be too heavy for deep water."

Cyrus rumpled his hair. "There seems to be more to submarine cables than I had realized. Now, about this St. Lawrence cable—we want to lay it this summer. Can you help me there?"

Mr. Brett nodded. "I can recommend the firm to make it for you. Glass, Elliot and Company. I can recommend a man to lay it for you. Samuel Canning. Good man, Canning. He's been with me on some of my adventures. And misadventures. He knows a lot of things not to do, too. How about it, Mr. Field? Maybe if you saw them making submarine cable you'd understand a little better what we're up against."

"Fine! Could we go to Glass, Elliot—"

"First we'll go to the Gutta-Percha Company. They'll make the core."

"That's just the copper wire, isn't it?" Cyrus asked. "I've seen it. I won't need to waste your time—"

"Copper is the heart of the cable, of course. But for submarine cable the copper has to be protected. So they coat it with gutta-percha. It's the rubbery sap of a tree from Malay. Best insulation we've found. In fact, if we hadn't learned about gutta-percha, I doubt if we'd ever have had submarine cable."

At the gutta-percha works Mr. Brett led the way to a tank. "Here's where we begin coating the copper with the gutta-percha."

Cyrus watched the bright copper wire run into the tank and come out covered with a dull, rubbery layer.

"When that coat is dry," Mr. Brett said, "they'll run it through another tank for a second coat. When the second coat is dry they'll give it a third coat."

"Couldn't they put on the gutta-percha in one thick layer?" Cyrus asked. "Save a lot of time."

"You might save time and lose the cable," Mr. Brett told him. "Every mile, every fathom, every *inch* of that copper must be protected from water. So we make sure the copper is at the dead center of the gutta-percha coatings."

"Submarine cable seems to be quite a problem."

Mr. Brett's eyes twinkled. "Yes, Mr. Field. Quite a problem."

"But when you do put the gutta-percha on in three layers you're sure of it?"

"Not always. We run underwater tests on every two-mile length of the core. Just to be sure there is no defect."

"But what could happen after all that folderol of putting on the coating in three layers?"

"There might be an air bubble in one layer of the gutta-percha. Any number of things can happen."

"But—but—" Cyrus could only repeat, "Quite a problem!"

At the Glass, Elliot plant he saw the copper core being made into cable. Quite a dizzy process to watch. One machine had a flat circular platform with reels full of yarn around the edge. The platform was turning, carrying the reels at a dizzy pace, and the reels were whirling on their own spindles, too. The gutta-percha covered core came up through a hole in the center of the platform, and the spinning reels fed a tightly twisted wrapping of yarn onto it.

"Worse than a merry-go-round," Cyrus remarked.

"It's the padding to protect the gutta-percha," Mr. Brett said. "So the iron wires of the sheathing can't cut into it. Then, after the yarn is soaked in a tar compound to protect it, we're ready for the sheathing."

Another dizzy process to watch, with a whirling platform carrying spinning reels of iron wire.

"And now it's done?" Cyrus asked.

"Not quite."

"But what in heaven's name is left to do? You've protected the copper with gutta-percha, and protected the gutta-percha with yarn, and protected the yarn with tar, and protected the whole thing with iron sheathing—"

"Then we run the cable through another tar compound to protect the iron from rust. Quite a touchy process. We have to be careful that the tar compound isn't too hot. That could destroy the insulation. Soften the gutta-percha, so that the copper could get off center. When the cable is running through the tar bath, if anything goes wrong and the cable stops running, we've probably ruined a spot of it."

"Then what do you do?"

"Cut the cable, take out the spot we're suspicious of, and make a splice. That's an interesting process. Perhaps you'd like to see that some day."

"How about now?"

"We won't have time today," Mr. Brett said. "It takes the jointers an hour or two to make a splice."

"An hour or two? Just to join two pieces of cable?"

"Yes, Mr. Field. That's like everything else about submarine cable. Quite a problem."

There was another man Cyrus met in England and liked on sight, just as he had liked John Brett—Isambord Brunel, engineer and shipbuilder. "The Little Giant," men called him. At first glance Cyrus noticed only Brunel's tall silk hat and his big cigar. Then he saw the man's eyes. They were like the eyes of Daniel Webster. No man would ever forget them.

"I've known your name a long time," Cyrus told him, "ever since you built the *Great Western.*"

"Wait till you see the ship I'm building now!" Brunel said. "She'll make any other ship in the world look like a tugboat!" He took Cyrus to see the great ship. "There, Mr. Field, is the ship to lay your Atlantic cable!"

"When will she be done?"

"We'll launch her by the end of fifty-seven. Then of

course it'll take several months before she's ready for her maiden voyage."

"Too long to wait!" Cyrus said. "But I'll promise you this! When your ship makes her maiden voyage I'll send my congratulations over the Atlantic cable!"

They shook hands on it, and Cyrus went to talk with Samuel Canning about laying the St. Lawrence cable.

They'd need to ship the cable from England to Newfoundland by early July, Mr. Canning said, and be ready to lay it before mid-August at the latest. Weather on the North Atlantic . . .

Evidently Mr. Canning had heard of the tour of the cable plant. He grinned as he added, "Yes, Mr. Field. Quite a problem."

Chapter 7

A Time Calm Enough—

ONE BRIGHT AUGUST MORNING CYRUS STOOD WITH PETER Cooper on the deck of the paddle steamer *James Adger,* watching as one carriage after another drew up at Pier Four. More than four dozen guests were embarking from New York to go to Port aux Basques, an isolated little harbor on the southwest coast of Newfoundland, to watch the laying of the St. Lawrence cable.

Mary could not make the trip; a little son was "brand-new," as Fanny said, but Gracie and Alice were there, listening in a glow as people came aboard and shook hands with their father:

"Congratulations, Mr. Field!"

"My, you look happy!"

"How nice of you to invite me!"

Porters shouldered their way through the merrymakers with boxes, portmanteaus, and trunks.

"Enough cargo," Mr. Cooper remarked, "to supply the Newfoundland work crews for a month."

Cyrus grinned and winked at his daughters. "Remember, sir, we have ladies with us. More than a dozen. And when we go on to St. John's for the celebration—"

"Of course," Mr. Cooper said. "A different gown for every occasion." He watched another mountain of luggage arrive. "Do you suppose we should have chartered a tender? To accompany the *James Adger* and carry the luggage?"

They saw John Mullaly of the *Herald,* and Bayard Taylor of the *Tribune,* alighting from carriages.

"Good to have the press represented, isn't it?" Cyrus asked. "So far we haven't had much publicity."

"Just as well, perhaps," Mr. Cooper said. "I'm afraid most people still think we're crackbrained dreamers."

Cyrus shook hands with the reporters. "So glad you could make it!"

"I couldn't miss it!" Mr. Taylor declared. "I've a feeling this is the first step in the wonder of the century!"

The first step? Cyrus thought back over the last year and a half, but he only smiled. "Right you are. The Atlantic cable is casting its shadow before it."

Mr. Taylor cocked his head. "Nicely put! I must remember that!"

They sailed. The masts and spars and steeples of New York disappeared. For three hours Cyrus moved among their guests. Then he excused himself and went to his cabin. A little paper work, he said. He wasn't going to put a damper on the occasion by letting anybody see him turn pale green!

By the time they entered the harbor of Port aux Basques, he was the liveliest passenger on board. A boat came out to meet them, and Cyrus recognized Samuel Canning.

"Hello, there! Welcome to the party!" he called.

Unsmiling, Mr. Canning lifted his hand in salute.

When he came aboard, he spoke in a quick undertone. "Could we go to your cabin, please?"

Bewildered, Cyrus led the way. In the cabin, he asked, "Trouble?"

"Close the door, please." Mr. Canning waited; then he said, "The cable ship hasn't arrived."

"What! But I thought she was to sail by—"

"The *Sarah* sailed from England before I did. July the third."

"But that's over a month ago! It couldn't take that long to reach Newfoundland!"

"That's what's worrying me," Mr. Canning said.

"You think—"

"A ship with cable aboard is very hard to handle. All that dead weight. If the *Sarah* hit rough seas—if the cable broke loose from its shoring—I've been on a cable ship in a storm. It's as though you were trying to protect something that wanted to kill you. Storms on the Mediterranean are bad enough. But storms on the North Atlantic . . ." He shook his head.

"What can we do?" Cyrus asked.

"Wait. And hope. Frankly, it's a mighty slim hope. If a really bad storm hit the *Sarah* I'm afraid she's lost. No ship of her tonnage, with that much cable aboard . . . There is something you can do, Mr. Field."

"Anything!"

"Take your party on to St. John's. Entertain the dignitaries."

"You mean—give parties—have a general jollification—when we don't know whether or not the *Sarah* is lost?"

"If the *Sarah* is lost will you abandon the plan for the Atlantic cable?"

"Of course not!"

"Then your good-will voyage to St. John's is important. And—I don't have to tell you, Mr. Field—chin up. It won't be easy. But it's important. I've talked with the people of Newfoundland. About you and your telegraph company. They believe in you. And their good will is very important. So—chin up. I suppose that's the hardest thing a promoter has to do—to keep up the spirits of other people when his hopes are in the bottom of his shoes. But—"

"St. John's it is," Cyrus said. "I'll send Mr. Gisborne and Mr. Morse in to talk to you. And Mr. Cooper. Meantime I'll put over the idea of a jolly little jaunt to St. John's!"

In the lounge he explained about the slight change in plans. It would have been easier to smile if he could have kept from thinking about the *Sarah*. He had heard too much about handling a cable ship in a storm. If the shoring on the cable coil gave way, and tons of cable went crashing to leeward . . .

"But we *are* going to St. John's?" one of the ladies asked. "If I've bought two new gowns for nothing I'll wring your neck!"

He assured her she would get to wear both gowns.

"I hope there won't be too much delay," a man said. "It would be quite an inconvenience to me."

Cyrus apologized for the possible inconvenience. Where was the *Sarah?* How could a ship spend more than a month just getting to Newfoundland?

"I wonder if we'll have any rough weather on the way to St. John's," a man said.

"Oh, I've never seen a storm at sea!" One of the ladies was all agog. "Be rather exciting, wouldn't it?"

Cyrus kept his hands behind him so they could not see his clenched fists. "Perhaps," he said, "if we can't order up a storm, we can arrange for some northern lights."

The trip to St. John's was quite jolly. The welcome in St. John's was warm:

"What courage your company has!"

"What American go-ahead!"

"Laying the St. Lawrence cable before the land line is done!"

"But you know, when you settled the debts of the old company, we decided we could depend on you!"

"You're really in this to the death, aren't you?"

Cyrus flinched at the word, but smiled. "We'll see it through."

He smiled through all the parties, listened to all the speeches, responded to all the toasts, and bowed to all the applause.

The eighteenth of August they embarked for the

return to Port aux Basques. A strong southwest wind brought a long, rolling swell. The *James Adger* wallowed. Cyrus excused himself. Some work in his cabin, he said.

At dawn two days later he managed to stay on deck by hanging onto the rail. Off the starboard bow he saw the loom of Cape Ray.

He called to the lookout. "Any sail?"

Not a vessel in sight.

About noon they made the rocky point off Port aux Basques.

He called again. "Any sail?"

The lookout reported a ship.

Cyrus gripped the rail until his knuckles whitened. "What ship is she?"

The lookout could not tell yet. After a dragging wait he reported it was the company's supply ship, the *Victoria.*

Another wait. The lookout yelled, "Sail ho-o-o-o! It's the *Sarah!*"

Cyrus didn't know whether to throw up his hat and yell or go down on his knees.

Again a boat brought Mr. Canning to the *James Adger.* This time he did not come aboard. He only suggested that perhaps Mr. Field would like to go to the *Sarah* with him.

Cyrus didn't ask questions. He scrambled down the ladder to the boat. "Thank God she made it!"

"Just," Mr. Canning said.

Even though Cyrus expected to see signs of a hard voyage he stared appalled at the wreckage aboard the *Sarah.*

The captain of the little vessel moved and spoke as a man in a daze. "Forty-eight days of it! Forty-eight bloomin' days! Trying to fight the Atlantic with eighty-five miles of cable in the hold. Never again!"

Eighty-five miles of cable? What would happen to a ship trying to handle sixteen hundred miles?

Mr. Canning's eyes begged Cyrus to say the right thing.

Cyrus wrung the captain's hand. "Thanks to your courage and seamanship we'll lay the St. Lawrence cable!"

The captain spoke flatly. "Not for a week you won't. Take that long to untangle the mess and repair the paying-out gear."

Cyrus fought down his impatience. "I know you'll do your best. And when the *Sarah* is ready to pay out the cable, the *James Adger* will be ready to tow her. Everything will be fine!"

The captain of the *James Adger* growled over the delay. "It's coming up a blow."

Cyrus turned his face to seaward. "I don't feel anything."

The captain snorted. "You won't—till it's too late. But the barometer is falling."

It was near—too near—the end of August when the *Sarah* was ready to lay the St. Lawrence cable.

Cyrus went to the *Sarah,* and stood by Mr. Canning to watch the paying out of the cable.

A mile—two miles—five—ten—ran into the sea. Cyrus could not take his eyes off it. His chest ached from holding his breath.

Mr. Canning glanced up, then turned back to his machine. "Better relax, Mr. Field. If you can't live through this, what'll you do when we lay the Atlantic cable?"

Fifteen miles—twenty— Almost a fourth of it down!

Canning was right, Cyrus thought. He must relax. He'd think of the day when all this preliminary work would be completed. The land line across Newfoundland done, and the St. Lawrence cable laid. An unbroken line of communication from New York to St. John's!

That was the thing to think about! And then . . .

He was in the middle of a thought when the gale struck.

For half an hour the *Sarah* fought the hawser at her bow and the weight of the cable astern, as a crazed animal would fight a tether. Another five minutes . . . ten . . . For almost an hour they held on. But it was hopeless. Mr. Canning gave the order. They cut the cable to save the ship.

Heartsick Cyrus watched the end splash into the

water. A year's delay. It would be next summer before they could make another attempt. And how much delay would this mean in getting backing for the Atlantic cable? News of this fiasco wasn't going to help. And word would spread all over the country. Four dozen disappointed guests. Not to mention the press.

Why, oh, why did I want to make such a big affair out of this? Why didn't I keep my mouth shut until the job was done? Why didn't I . . .

He knew well enough why. Before they could lay the Atlantic cable they needed publicity. They needed to rouse England and America, both, to do that. They needed the press to tell the world that their "crack-brained dream" was a possibility. Reporters to tell the world . . .

They'd be telling the world now, all right. And the world would be wagging its head.

"An Atlantic cable? Hah! What happened to your St. Lawrence cable?"

"How about it? Was the Atlantic cable casting its shadow before it?"

"How about it, Mr. Field?"

Chapter 8

A Wire Long Enough—

WHEN THE GALE HAD BLOWN ITSELF OUT AND CYRUS could return to the *James Adger* he went in search of his daughters. They were in their cabin. Gracie avoided his eyes. Alice began to cry. He sat down between them, and put an arm around each.

"I'm sorry," he said. "Come on, now. Dry your tears and get ready for dinner."

"I'm not going to eat with anybody on this ship!" Alice sobbed. "I hate them! Calling my f-father a f-fool!"

"There, there!" He patted her shoulder. He couldn't think of anything else to say, so he said it again. "There, there!"

"Are you going on with it?" Gracie asked.

"Of course. Next summer will be different! Just wait and see!"

He went to the lounge. Bayard Taylor and John Mullaly were waiting for him.

"What now, Mr. Field? What do you plan to do?"

Cyrus had the answer to that. He had heard it first twenty years ago, by acres of smoking ruins. "Charge it to profit and loss and start over." He hoped he looked more confident than he felt. Another trip to England, another cable to order, another attempt to lay it. And what would happen then?

The next summer when he embarked once more to meet Mr. Canning at Port aux Basques Cyrus thought of the contrast and smiled wryly. No gay party this time, no laughing crowds, no mountains of luggage. If they had to face another fiasco . . .

This time they laid the St. Lawrence cable without a hitch. Why, oh, why couldn't it have been this way last year?

Mr. Gisborne was at Port aux Basques. Cyrus was so shocked at his appearance that he had to ask him over again what he had said. Great Scott, the fellow had aged ten years!

"I said," Mr. Gisborne repeated, "that we'll finish the land line by October."

"Congratulations!"

Mr. Gisborne didn't smile. "Then, Mr. Field, I shall resign as engineer. My doctor tells me I've had enough field work for a while. I'll try to find you a good superintendent. You'll *need* a good man," he added grimly. "A mighty good man."

"A man to work the lines?" Cyrus asked.

"A man to keep the lines in working order. That climate and that terrain! You'll always need a crew in Newfoundland. In the last month . . ."

Cyrus listened to what had been happening. Overhead lines, he declared, had one thing in common with submarine lines. They were quite a problem.

Tireder than he would admit, even to himself, he went home.

"Cyrus!" Mary stared at him aghast. "I've never seen you so tired! Even last summer when the cable failed, you—"

"I guess it's just catching up with me," he said. "It's been quite a two years and a half to go through. You might say I started out on a hundred-yard dash and found I had to run a marathon instead."

"And now?" she asked.

"The Atlantic cable."

"Another trip to England! You poor— Please, Cyrus—"

"Yes?"

"Will you try to remember that this may be a marathon, too? Try not to—"

"What you want to say is 'slow down'?"

She smiled. "I suppose so. Silly of me, isn't it? How soon will you have to leave?"

"I've already booked passage and I've written John Brett for an appointment. I'll see him first."

"An Atlantic cable?" John Brett nodded. "Yes, I'm interested. I think that in three or four years we might—"

"In three or four years! I intend to see that cable laid next summer!"

"Oh, come now, Mr. Field! Just to manufacture over two thousand miles of cable—"

Cyrus broke in. "It's only a little over sixteen hundred miles from Ireland to Newfoundland."

"But we have to allow slack. I'd say twenty-five hundred miles is the lowest safe figure. We don't know how many mountains and chasms we might have to cross."

"When Berryman and Dayman sounded that route they didn't find—"

Mr. Brett was patient. "Mr. Field, their soundings were taken about ten miles apart. Between those soundings no man knows what we might find."

"Then why didn't they take them closer together? Every mile? Every half mile? Why didn't they—"

"Maybe," Mr. Brett suggested, "because it takes six hours to make one sounding."

"Oh."

"Deep-sea soundings are like submarine cable, Mr. Field. Quite a problem."

Cyrus paced the floor. "All right! So we'll need twenty-five hundred miles of cable! We'll order twenty-five hundred miles of cable! We'll—"

"Of *what* cable, Mr. Field? We don't know what sort of cable we'll need."

"Then how can we find out?"

"By tests and experiments. Dozens of them—maybe hundreds. Then, after we have found the cable to meet our needs, we'll have to find ships big enough to lay it. When the *Great Eastern* is ready for sea—"

"The cable will be laid and working!" Cyrus declared. "If one ship can't lay it, use two—four—ten! Any number we need!"

"And try to make half a dozen splices in the middle of the Atlantic? Where the water may be two or three miles deep? Try to stop a ship and keep her steady enough not to snap the cable that's already laid? When there'll be a drag of heaven knows how many tons on that cable? No, Mr. Field. We might divide the cable between two ships, and make one mid-ocean splice before we start paying out, but we could never—"

"Then that's it! Two ships to carry the cable and—"

Mr. Brett was still patient. "*What* two ships, Mr. Field? There isn't a merchant ship afloat that could carry half that cable."

"Oh . . ." The sentence from Maury's letter came back to Cyrus:

> Nor do I pretend to consider the question of finding a time calm enough, a sea smooth enough, a wire long enough, a ship big enough . . .

The matter of "a time calm enough" had become a grim reality. Why hadn't he ever thought about the rest of that sentence?

"The only ships big enough to handle even half of a cable that long," Mr. Brett said, "would be British or American naval vessels. And whether or not our navies could spare them—"

"We shouldn't need them very long, should we?" Cyrus asked. "A month ought to—"

"It would take more than a month to get a vessel ready to carry cable. We have to practically rebuild the cargo-carrying space, to make room for tanks to carry the cable. Tanks with walls strong enough to withstand tons of pressure when a ship rolls. And there's a lot of waste space in a tank. In the center we have to allow room for a core to coil the cable around. If we don't use a core the layers of cable—sailors call them 'flakes'—might slip and get tangled in each other."

"I've seen rope laid out on the deck of a ship, just looped back and forth, one layer on top of another," Cyrus said. "It seemed to pay out all right without tangling."

"Not submarine cable," John Brett said. "It has to be coiled down by hand, row after row, flake after flake, without a single kink anywhere in all the miles of cable. So even after a ship was rebuilt with tanks to carry half of an Atlantic cable, it would take at least a month to coil down the cable into her tanks."

"A month just to coil down a cable? I can't see what in the name of sense—"

"Some day you will." John Brett smiled. "Yes, Mr.

Field, it's quite a problem."

"But you are interested?" Cyrus asked.

"Definitely. And I think Charles Bright would be. I hope so. His help would be invaluable. He's the chief engineer of our Magnetic Telegraph Company. He and his brother have patented over forty inventions for installing, testing, and working telegraph lines. And Charles Bright has installed over seven thousand miles of lines for Magnetic—overhead, underground, and submarine. So he's not only an inventor. He's a practical engineer."

"Then let's see him!"

"Heaven knows when we can get hold of him. Perhaps in a week or two—"

"Why not tomorrow night for dinner?"

John Brett gave Cyrus a long, level stare. At last he smiled. "Are all Americans in such a hurry? Or are you exceptional?"

Cyrus grinned. "I've heard it hinted I'm worse than the average. Twenty years ago my brother called me 'young man in a hurry.' He's repeated it several times since. Now, about tomorrow night . . ."

The next morning John Brett sent a note to Cyrus. They would meet Charles Bright for dinner that evening. At eight o'clock.

At a quarter of eight Cyrus entered the restaurant. A tall lad unfolded his length from a chair and ambled over. "Mr. Field? I'm Charles Bright."

Evidently the engineer's son. Cyrus shook hands. "Well, well! I'm glad you could join us. John Brett and your father ought to be along soon."

The young man's smile widened to a grin. "I'm Magnetic's engineer, Mr. Field."

"But—but—John Brett said you'd patented over forty inventions? And—"

"Oh, I'm older than I look. Twenty-three. And I got into telegraphy when I was only fifteen. So I've rather grown up with it."

"Just as a matter of curiosity," Cyrus asked, "when did you take out your first patent?"

"Not until fifty-two."

"I see. Just an old man of nineteen when you started inventing?"

"Oh, we'd been inventing things right along. But it costs two hundred pounds to take out a patent. We didn't have money enough before fifty-two. One good thing about our patent law, though, we can patent a group of related inventions all for the same fee."

"And how many inventions did you patent at that hoary age?"

"Twenty-four."

John Brett joined them. "So you've met our chief engineer, Mr. Field?" The three laughed together and went in to dinner.

Before they had given their order Cyrus was talking of an Atlantic cable. Before the first course came he said, "How about it, Mr. Bright? Do you think you'd be interested in working on it?"

"Oh, I've already been working on it. Last summer —I couldn't go myself—but I sent my brother Edward and a crew to sound the shoreline off the west coast of Ireland. Hunting for the best place to land an Atlantic cable. I wanted to find a spot if possible where four conditions would obtain: It couldn't be a bay where ships were accustomed to anchoring. We've had too much trouble with anchors getting caught in cables and breaking them. Yet the place must be fairly protected from storms, so we could land a cable. Then we'd need a smooth bottom for the approach of the shore end of the cable, and deeper water offshore free from rocks. It took quite a bit of hunting. Valentia Bay is the best possibility."

Cyrus felt his jaw sagging and closed his mouth.

"And I've been thinking about how to run tests for signaling through more than two thousand miles of submarine cable," the young man went on. "I believe I can connect the different wires in some of my underground lines into a continuous circuit, and get a fair approximation. You see, overhead and underground lines react differently. With overhead lines our main problem is resistance. But in an underground line there's also capacitance. Now in submarine lines that same effect obtains, so—" Cyrus must have looked as bewildered as he felt. Charles Bright broke off. "I'm afraid I'm boring you?"

"No, that's not the word for it. Go on."

"Glass and Elliot would have to run dozens of tests —perhaps hundreds—before they could build a cable to span the Atlantic. Heavy enough to sink, light enough to handle, flexible enough not to break easily, and strong enough to bear several miles of its own weight. Of course, under water it won't weigh as much as it does in air, but there will be the drag of ocean currents on it, and— You're sure I'm not boring you, Mr. Field? People say that when I get started I never know when to stop."

"Not a bit bored," Cyrus declared. "Just bewildered. Now, let me catch up. The first thing is to have Glass and Elliot build samples of cable to get it heavy enough, light enough—"

"No, Mr. Field. First we must experiment with signaling through two thousand miles of submerged line. Determine the weight of copper and the weight of gutta-percha we'll need for the core. Then we'll start thinking about a cable strong enough to stand the strain."

"Tests on the core, eh? How long will they take? And then the tests on the cable? How long will all the tests take?"

Mr. Bright shrugged. "Who knows? We've never done it yet. The longest armored cable we've laid isn't two hundred miles long. When we talk of laying more than two thousand miles of cable in water two or three miles deep—well, it's going to take the engineering brains of England to solve that problem."

"I'm no engineer," Cyrus said. "But I can be getting the ships we'll need."

"How do you know what sort of ships we'll need till we—"

"If we ask for the biggest vessels the navies have, that ought to take care of it," Cyrus told him. "By the time you scientists settle on the cable, we can have everything else ready to go. If we want to lay the cable next summer—"

"Mr. Field!" Charles Bright stared. "Have you the faintest idea of the problems involved?"

"Scientific? Not the faintest." Cyrus grinned. "I didn't build one mile of the Newfoundland line, or make one foot of the St. Lawrence cable. I'm merely the man who raised the money to do it."

"And," Mr. Brett said quietly, "the man who got the exclusive rights to land submarine cable in Newfoundland for fifty years. When you ask for English co-operation, you do have something to offer. But whether we can make enough people believe in the possibility of an Atlantic cable . . . Perhaps if we talk to our scientists . . ."

They did. It seemed to Cyrus they must have talked to half the scientists in England. Many said, "Impossible!" Some said, "Perhaps, in a few years." When Cyrus talked of laying the Atlantic cable the next summer no one said anything. Men only stared.

When they could lay an Atlantic cable, or how, the three of them did not know, but they drew up an agreement:

> Mutually, and on equal terms we engage to exert ourselves for the purpose of forming a Company for establishing and working of electric telegraphic communication between Newfoundland and Ireland, such Company to be called the Atlantic Telegraph Company. . . .
>
> John Brett
> Charles T. Bright
> Cyrus W. Field

Mr. Morse, who happened to be in England, and Dr. Whitehouse, physician turned electrician, spent long hours with Charles Bright at the London quarters of Magnetic. Midnight to dawn, when the telegraph lines were free, they ran test after test.

"Interesting pair," Cyrus remarked to John Brett. "Samuel Morse, artist turned inventor; Dr. Whitehouse, physician turned electrician."

"Most men in telegraphy today were something else first," Mr. Brett said, "unless, like Charles Bright, they are so young they grew up with it. He still surprises you?"

"He amazes me! Well, while they are experimenting on their lines, I'm going after the backing of our governments. We'll get that moving so—"

John Brett smiled wryly. "I wish you luck. I remember when I petitioned the British government for backing to lay a cable from Dover to Calais. Twenty-four miles. I laid that cable five years later. Now you want backing to lay a cable from Ireland to Newfoundland. Two thousand land miles. How long do you think it will take you to get it?"

"A month," Cyrus said. "Maybe two months if they do a lot of talking."

John Brett didn't say anything.

Less than two months later Cyrus laid a letter before his partners. The British government had promised:

The aid of ships to take any further soundings needed.

Naval vessels to help lay the cable.

As soon as the cable was working, and so long as it worked, a guarantee of 14,000 pounds a year.

In return for that, the company promised that the messages of the British government would have priority over all others, unless the American government entered into a similar agreement. In that case, the messages of the two governments would have priority in the order in which they arrived at the cable stations.

After a silence John Brett said, "And when you get

home you'll ask the same sort of terms from your government?"

"Wait till I get home? I've already sent a letter! By the time I get home they'll have written a bill, presented it to Congress, and passed it in both houses!"

John Brett shot a look at Charles Bright. "I've heard that his brother called him 'a man in a hurry.' "

Cyrus laughed with them. "With this sort of co-operation from our governments, we'll raise the rest of our capital in jig time."

Busy weeks followed for the three of them in the offices of the Magnetic Telegraph Company in Liverpool, Manchester, and London. With John Brett, a director, and Charles Bright, their chief engineer, talking of the cable, Cyrus found the directors and stockholders of Magnetic solidly back of them.

"You gentlemen are the exception to prove the rule," he said once. "Prophets with honor in your own company!"

By early December they had raised their capital—three hundred and fifty shares, at five thousand dollars each. Cyrus subscribed for eighty-eight shares—a fourth of the capital.

"Not that I intend to hold them all," he said. "But Americans will want a part in this enterprise!"

In early December the shareholders met and elected their board of directors. They appointed Dr. Whitehouse electrician and Charles Bright engineer.

"And now," one of the directors asked, "what about the cable?"

"We've given the Gutta-Percha Company of London a tentative okay for the core," Dr. Whitehouse said. "Much heavier than anything ever made before. More than a hundred pounds of copper and three hundred pounds of gutta-percha to the mile."

Charles Bright shook his head. "Not heavy enough. We ought to have more than three hundred pounds of copper and—"

Dr. Whitehouse interrupted. "Not for submarine cable. The smaller the copper conductor the better. The Leyden-jar effect, you know. Charging and discharging. The heavier the conductor, the more electricity it would take to charge it. Don't you see?"

"No! I absolutely don't agree with you!"

Dr. Whitehouse smiled. "Well, my dear boy, Michael Farraday does. And so does Professor Morse. What have you to say to that?"

Charles Bright flushed. "Just this! I've laid and worked more submarine cables than they have!"

The argument went on, with Charles Bright hurling facts and figures, and Dr. Whitehouse beginning every protest with "my dear boy."

The directors got into the argument, too. "After all," one said, "we have two problems here: engineering—the laying of the cable; electrical—the working of the cable after it is laid. It's your responsibility,

Mr. Bright, to see that the cable can be laid. To test the strength of the armor—all that. It's Dr. Whitehouse's responsibility to work the cable after it is laid."

The directors voted; they sided with Dr. Whitehouse. The order for the core would stand. When their engineer was satisfied with the strength tests of the cable, the cable companies could start work.

The next day Cyrus was on shipboard, facing one more wintertime crossing of the Atlantic. He got home Christmas Day.

"I'm glad that's done," he said. "Now Bright and Whitehouse can take over. I'm not going to think of cable till . . ."

Two letters from Newfoundland awaited him. He opened the first. Newfoundland's charter with the American company, he read, did not give the privilege of landing submarine cables to the Atlantic Telegraph Company. Someone had better come before the legislature immediately . . .

He opened the other letter. The land line across Newfoundland was a shambles. One break after another. The superintendent had given up in despair. Someone had better get up there fast, or there would not be anything left to come up there about!

"Oh, Cyrus!" Mary pleaded. "Not another . . . You'll have to go?"

"By the first boat," he said.

Chapter 9

A Ship Big Enough—

A MAN FROM ST. JOHN'S THAT CYRUS KNEW WAS A FELlow-passenger on the trip to Newfoundland. "Well, Mr. Field! We meet again! Horrible time of year for this trip, isn't it? Rough—even for an old salt like you."

Cyrus didn't enlighten the man about the kind of "old salt" he was. Maybe the trip wouldn't be as rough as the crossing from England had been.

It was worse. Cyrus never did find his sea legs. In St. John's they carried him from the boat to the hotel and put him to bed.

"It's just this stupid business of getting seasick," he told the doctor. "I'll be all right tomorrow. I'll—"

"My dear man, this is more than seasickness. And you aren't going to get over it in a day or two. Or a week or two. You belong in a hospital! It'll be at least a month before—"

"I can't take time to go to the hospital!"

When he could sit up without the room going around too fast, Cyrus got to work. When he booked passage for home a month later he had ironed out things with the legislature of Newfoundland, and untangled the mess of the land line. A new superintendent was in charge—young Mr. Mackay. Only twenty-two. Even younger than Charles Bright. But, like Charles Bright, he had grown up with telegraphy. And there was a look in his level eyes that said he'd never give up.

Cyrus was packing for the trip home when the doctor stormed in, talking as he came. "Mr. Field! It's utterly out of the question for you to undertake a sea voyage now. You belong—"

"Nonsense. Can't see what you're fussing about. You prescribe rest. I promise you I'll get it. Stay flat on my back all the way home."

"You'll be flat on your back longer than that," the doctor said.

Cyrus got up from his berth only to leave the boat in New York, and was ready to go back to bed when he got home. He paused at his desk to riffle through his mail. A letter from Senator Seward caught his eye.

Good lord! The cable bill! A good thing someone was looking after it! He certainly hadn't had time to think about it. Smiling, he opened the letter and began to read. His smile faded. The cable bill was meeting bitter opposition.

He was on the train for Washington before he opened the rest of his mail. One letter was from a director in London.

. . . Charles Bright is working around the clock, running tests on samples of cable, and inspecting naval vessels. A good thing the United States will be furnishing a vessel to lay half the cable! . . .

Cyrus wondered.

In Washington he met with a harried Senator Seward and a very grave Lieutenant Maury. Dumfounded, he listened.

"But we're not asking the United States to do anything that the British government isn't ready and willing to do!" he protested. "If the British—"

"Mention the British," Mr. Seward told him, "and you shake a red rag at a bull."

"But can't they see what a cable will mean?" Cyrus asked. "Can't they—"

"No, Mr. Field. They can't—or won't. Not enough of them."

"But it would be a disgrace for the United States not to have a hand in—"

"You don't have to persuade us, Mr. Field," Mr. Maury said. "Tackle the opposition."

"I'll do it! From now till that bill comes up for debate I'll talk to every congressman who will listen to me!"

Day after day he did talk to "every congressman who would listen." Some could not find time to see him. Some listened in grim-jawed silence. Some interrupted with bitter tirades against England. Every day he was more baffled.

What was the matter with his countrymen? Why couldn't he reach them? He had sewed up the rights with Newfoundland so that England must co-operate with America on the cable; he had raised and risked more than a million and a half dollars on the first steps; he had persuaded the English government to back the project, and to allow the United States equal privileges on the same terms. He had come home to his own people, triumphant, bearing gifts. And now his own people . . .

When the bill came up for debate he listened, heart-sick, and left the sessions in a daze. March 3, the last day of the session, the cable bill passed by one vote.

If Congress had wrangled bitterly, they came through handsomely. The United States would support the cable, when it was laid and working, on the same terms that England had granted. And the navy would furnish two of its finest ships to help lay the cable—the *Susquehanna* and the *Niagara.*

Captain Hudson invited Cyrus to visit the *Niagara* before they started work on her. He was glad to go. Maybe the sight of the ship would wipe the taste of Washington out of his mouth.

A ship's boat picked him up and carried him toward the *Niagara.*

"Biggest screw-propeller vessel in the world!" one of the sailors said proudly. "Overall length, three hundred and forty-five feet; beam, fifty-five feet. When we're under sail we can spread seven thousand yards of canvas. Under steam, we have three engines with cylinders seventy-two inches in diameter!"

Cyrus found himself thinking not of her size or her power, but her beauty. He thanked them and went aboard.

Captain Hudson seemed to understand how he felt. "Beautiful as a yacht, isn't she? Maybe because George Steers designed her. You know, he designed the *America,* that brought back that yachting cup from England." He chuckled. "Gave the British quite a shock, I suspect. And wait till they see the *Niagara!* Poor George Steers. Too bad he didn't live to see this day. To see his beautiful ship take part in the greatest achievement of the century!"

Cyrus gazed about at the gleaming metal, the polished wood, the spotless decks. He thought of the steamer that had laid the second St. Lawrence cable. A deck filled with clanking machinery, and everything smeared with tar. Poor Captain Hudson! he thought. How would he feel when they made a work horse of his proud ship?

It was mid-March before Cyrus got around to offering shares of Atlantic Telegraph Company stock in America. Just as well, he thought. While the debate was going on in Congress he couldn't have sold half the eighty-eight shares he held. But now that the debate was over, and the United States back of the cable, too . . .

He sold twenty-seven shares. Besides all his stock in the Newfoundland company, he was saddled with three hundred and five thousand dollars' worth of Atlantic Telegraph Company stock. How could he tell Mary? She'd be worried sick.

But Mary astounded him. "Shame on them! When the cable's laid they'll be falling all over themselves to buy stock. It'd serve them right if you wouldn't sell them any!"

He hugged her, then admitted ruefully, "I seem to be a prophet without honor in my own country, don't I?"

Mary smiled faintly. "I suspect Mr. Holderby is saying, 'Mark my words! I always knew Cyrus Field would come to no good end!' "

Cyrus managed an answering smile. Mr. Holderby, he knew, wasn't the only one! He shrugged off the thought and went to his desk. He'd better catch up on his own affairs before he had to go back to England.

When he returned to England he went with Charles Bright to see the *Agamemnon.*

"She's a cable man's dream," Charles Bright said. "Engines very far astern, leaving a magnificent hold. Forty-five feet square by twenty feet deep. She'll be able to carry practically all her cable in one tank."

"What's her tonnage?" Cyrus asked.

"Something over three thousand."

Wait till they see the *Niagara!* Cyrus thought. Over five thousand tons!

The *Niagara* arrived in the Thames, and the English flocked to stare. For days throngs crowded aboard to see her. The crew showed their visitors around proudly. Too bad, they said, they didn't have their guns aboard. Twelve Dahlgrens, each weighing fourteen tons. Just twelve guns, but a broadside from them could sink anything afloat.

Only Captain Hudson did not seem too happy. He shook his head over the way they had wrecked his beautiful ship to make room for the cable. Stores moved, bulkheads knocked out, beams braced with double stays to hold the hundreds of tons of weight. Big as the *Niagara* was, it had taken a lot of "scooping out," he said, to make room for the cable tanks. No, they had no place for one big tank. They had three. The smallest tank, on the berth deck, was twenty-seven feet across, the orlop deck tank was thirty-eight feet, and the tank in the hold was forty feet.

"Some of the officers want to meet you," Captain Hudson said. "We'll probably find them in the wardroom. That's the only place they haven't wrecked."

Just as Cyrus and the captain started below Charles Bright came aboard.

The captain mustered a smile. "Welcome aboard, Mr. Bright! Come below and we'll—"

"Captain Hudson," the young engineer said, "we're going to have to have more room on the *Niagara*."

"More room?" The captain was still polite but he had lost his smile. "We've stripped the decks for your machinery; we've gutted the ship for your cable. What else do you need?"

"Those three tanks won't hold your share of the cable, sir. We'll have to have another tank at least as big as that on the orlop deck."

"But there's no place for another tank!" the captain protested. "I've got to have room for provisions for more than four hundred men! I've got to have room for five hundred tons of coal. I've got to—"

"We'll need another tank, sir, at least thirty-eight feet in diameter."

Captain Hudson seemed to be counting to ten; then he spoke quietly. "Mr. Bright, I've handled cable—every kind of line—for more years than you are years old. There's no necessity for these tanks to hold the cable!"

Charles Bright spoke politely, too. "How would you suggest we carry it, sir?"

"We've plenty of open space on the deck. Just lay it there in neat flakes."

After a long silence, the engineer nodded. "Thank you for your suggestion. We'll try it, sir. I'll have some cable brought aboard. Your men can flake it down as you suggest. Then we'll try paying it out."

"That's the spirit!" Captain Hudson drew a gusty breath of relief. "Bring on the cable. I'll show you how to handle it."

The next day they brought ten miles of cable on board, and an officer directed the men about laying it on the deck.

Captain Hudson watched. "That's it! That's the idea!"

Mr. Bright said, "Yes, sir. And now we'll pay it out."

They hitched up a donkey engine, and began paying out. In ten minutes the cable was a hopeless tangle.

Captain Hudson stared across the mess at the young engineer. "Where do you propose to put that other tank?"

"Just aft of your coal bunkers and forward of your wardroom, sir."

"But we don't have thirty-eight feet of free space there!"

"I know, sir," Charles Bright agreed. "We'll have to knock out bulkheads and use part of your wardroom, sir."

Chapter 10

A Sea Smooth Enough—

CYRUS DID NOT GO ABOARD THE "NIAGARA" AGAIN FOR quite a while. When he saw Captain Hudson the poor man growled darkly that they had "scooped her out like a crab."

But old Ben Surrey told Cyrus that he really ought to see them coiling down the cable into the tanks of the *Niagara*. Ben was a cable man from way back. He'd made pit rope before submarine cable was ever dreamed of. He'd been a jointer on most of John Brett's cable-laying expeditions. Cyrus had seen Ben perform that long, delicate operation of splicing the cable. And, besides, Ben was cheerful. So Cyrus went with him to the *Niagara*.

On board, Cyrus looked about him at the mess. He remembered his visit to the ship at Brooklyn, and the clean sweep of the spar deck. Now he saw a tangle of geared wheels and drums that was the huge paying-out machine, the makeshift deckhouse they had built for the electricians' test room, a confusion of barrels, drums, buoys taller than a man, and coils of hawser.

Overhead, beams and pulleys, with wires running down through hatches to the decks below. And tar everywhere. If it had rained tar, Cyrus thought, it couldn't have smeared things more completely.

"Watch out for the tar," Ben said cheerfully. "Get against anything, you'll be marked for life. Proper stuff, though, to prevent rust."

Captain Hudson happened to be on board. He, too, looked around him at the mess. He only said, "Poor George Steers. I've changed my mind. Better that he didn't live to see this day."

Cyrus was relieved that he could say he'd promised to go to the tank with Ben. They went below to the berth deck, ten feet deeper to the orlop deck, and another fourteen feet farther down into the dark hold. They stood where they could look over the wooden wall of the huge forty-foot tank. They were twelve feet below the water line now. Even though four dozen candles and lamps were burning, the tank was a gloomy dungeon.

As his eyes grew accustomed to the darkness Cyrus could see the core in the center of the tank, a big cone that looked like the top of an extinct volcano. Iron hoops, a little bigger around than the cone, hung over it, and the cable ran down through a hatch above the center of the tank, and then between the iron hoops and the cone.

"Them hoops are fair-leaders," Ben said. "Keep the

cable from tangling. Just one kink in that cable and . . ." He grinned and spread his hands.

A few men were busy near the center of the tank. A dozen or so others lolled about.

They recognized Cyrus and Ben and waved tar-blackened hands. "The Knights of the Black Hand salute you!" they yelled.

"Seem to be a lot of men doing nothing," Cyrus remarked. "Must be two dozen men in there."

"Thirty." Ben grinned. "Lots of hurry-up-and-wait in a job like this. When they start coiling down the next flake, you'll find out what they're for. Takes a lot of hands to coil down three–four hundred miles of cable without a kink." He slapped one of the heavy stanchions that braced the wall of the tank. "And a lot of wood to hold it. Come a storm, if the ship rolled, and a few hundred tons of cable crashed through that wall . . ." He grinned and spread his hands again.

"A good thing the men who shored up the tank knew what they were doing, eh?" Cyrus remarked.

"We hope they did. But we can't be sure, can we? Nobody's tried to handle a thousand tons of cable in a North Atlantic storm. But–'hope for the best and be prepared for the worst.' That's what I always say." Ben looked into the tank. "Just ready for the next flake."

The coilers shoved their boxes and stools toward the wall of the tank and sat.

"Lower away!" the leader yelled.

The cable began to snake down between the fair-leaders and the cone. The leader started at a jog trot around the circle, paying out cable to each man as he passed him. When he had completed one round, he started the second. The coilers leaned forward, packing the second row smoothly against the first.

The leader trotted at a steady pace. A man with a high tenor voice began to wail a song. The coilers all joined in on the refrain:

"Lost . . . lost . . . down in the deep!
No . . . no . . . he never came home!
Weep . . . weep . . . O poor maiden, weep!
No . . . no . . . he never came home!"

Cyrus shivered. "Don't they know a more cheerful song?"

Ben stared. "What's the matter? It's got a good beat!" After a little he chuckled. "Guess you've had about enough, eh?"

When they climbed from the dark hold the song followed them, a ghostly echo:

"Lost . . . lost . . . down in the deep!
No . . . no . . . he never came home!"

"Watch out for the tar," Ben said again. "Good stuff, though. Besides protecting against rust. Keeps the flakes in even rows. Just tacky enough to keep one turn packed against the other. Not sticky enough to keep the cable from paying out. At least we hope it's not too sticky. Of course, we've never tried to pay out this much cable before, have we? If that tar is too sticky . . ."

"How long will it take to coil the cable into the tanks?" Cyrus asked.

"We got two crews, each coiling down about two miles an hour. We ought to do it in three–four weeks —even allowing for accidents."

"Accidents?"

"Oh, there's always accidents! I remember once—"

Cyrus thanked Ben for showing him around, but said he'd have to hurry along now.

That night he was a long time getting to sleep. Everything he had heard of that could ruin the cable ran through his mind:

"If the copper core gets off center, so the gutta-percha doesn't protect it . . ."

"One tiny air bubble in a layer of gutta-percha—when the tons of pressure hit it in the bottom of the ocean . . ."

"One drop of moisture on the gutta-percha—even a smear from a sweaty hand—when the tons of pressure hit it in the bottom of the ocean . . ."

"If we don't pay out enough cable to take care of hills and valleys, and we happen to leave it suspended across two peaks . . ."

"If the cable pays out too fast and we run out of cable before we reach port . . ."

"If one flake of cable gets tangled in the flake below . . ."

"One bad kink in a bight of cable . . ."

"Come a storm, if the ship rolled, and three–four hundred tons of cable crashed through the wall of the tank . . ."

And the song went around in his head:

"Lost . . . lost . . . down in the deep!"

It was less than a month before the cable expedition was to start that Cyrus met with the directors to find a new idea full blown: The ships of the Wire Squadron were not to meet in mid-ocean, make the splice, and steam in opposite directions; instead, the *Niagara* would lay the first half of the cable from Valentia; then they would make a mid-ocean splice, and the *Agamemnon* would lay her half from mid-ocean to Newfoundland. That way, the telegraph station at Valentia—and the directors in London—would be in touch with the expedition all the time.

Cyrus wasn't quite sure how the idea started. Probably, he decided, Dr. Whitehouse proposed it. The head electrician of the Atlantic Telegraph Company was not well enough to go with the expedition. At any rate, when Cyrus reached the meeting, Charles Bright and Dr. Whitehouse were in the thick of an argument.

"My dear boy," Dr. Whitehouse said, "you know how stormy Valentia Bay is. What if the cable ship approached Valentia, and it was too stormy to land the cable?"

"What of it?" Charles Bright answered. "We'd buoy the cable and wait for a calm day to make the splice! That's all! We've done it time and again with cables! In the North Sea we've buoyed cables ten to fifty miles from land and left them—sometimes for weeks—before we made the splice to the land end!"

"Now, my dear boy—"

Charles Bright didn't exactly turn his back on Dr. Whitehouse, but he did turn to the directors. "Please, gentlemen! If we start laying the cable from Valentia, when we reach mid-ocean there will be a strain of over two thousand fathoms of cable dragging at the brakes of the paying-out machine! What if we run into a storm? And have to stop the *Niagara,* and wait for a time calm enough to make the splice? When a ship must be stopped, and she does not have way on, she's at the mercy of the sea. The *Niagara* would be riding at anchor on that cable. Riding at anchor, in a storm, on a line about one inch thick! And what's more . . ."

He talked on and on. The directors listened. They promised to think over what he had said. They'd try to remember all the points he had made.

"You'll have it in writing!" Their engineer bit out the words. "My protest is going to be in the record!"

He wrote. The directors read. But the thought of being in touch with the Wire Squadron was too tempting. The order stood: The *Niagara* would start paying out her cable from Valentia.

Tuesday, August 4, was the day set for the landing of the shore end of the cable and the start of the expedition. Cyrus had seen that desolate spot where the cable would be brought ashore. He was glad they had already had dinners, speeches, and celebrations for the men of the Wire Squadron—something to cheer them on for the task ahead. There would not be many at Valentia Bay to see them off!

But Tuesday, in spite of a wind-driven mist and pounding seas, people were gathering by dawn. They stood there in the rain until word came that it was too stormy to land the cable.

Before dawn the next morning hundreds were coming from every direction—in carts, on horseback, and afoot, and in every kind of boat. By mid-morning two thousand were there. They waited all day.

It was almost sunset when they saw the boats approaching, and American sailors jumped out, wading ashore, dragging the hawser attached to the massive shore end of the cable.

With a wild cheer the people surged forward to help. Top hats and the tousled heads of peasants mingled in the mob. The Earl of Carlisle, Lord-Lieutenant of Ireland, was one of the first to grab hold of the hawser.

An officer from the *Niagara* saluted him and made the formal presentation.

Wild cheers drowned his words and the Lord-Lieutenant's smiling answer. The crowd grew quiet when a minister lifted his hands to pray:

"O Eternal Lord God, who alone spreadest out the heavens and rulest the raging of the sea, and whom the winds and the sea obey . . ."

As Cyrus listened to the prayer he remembered other words: *A time calm enough, a sea smooth enough . . .*

Even though the people knew the ships would not

weigh anchor until morning, they stayed. They helped drag the tarry cable up to the telegraph house. They called for a speech from the Lord-Lieutenant.

How simply and warmly he spoke to them, explaining the cable in terms of what it could mean to them:

"... If you wished to communicate some piece of intelligence straightway to your relatives across the wide world of waters—if you wished to tell those whom you know what would interest them in their heart of hearts, of a birth, or a marriage, or, alas, a death, among you, the cord, which we have now hauled up to the shore, will impart that tidings quicker than the flash of lightning. . . ."

Part of the time it seemed to Cyrus that the Earl of Carlisle was talking directly to him:

"... we ought still to remember that we must speak with the modesty of those who begin and not of those who close an experiment, and it behooves us to remember that the pathway to great achievement has frequently to be hewn out amidst risks and difficulties, and that preliminary failure is even the law and condition of the ultimate success. . . ."

Preliminary failure . . . Cyrus thought of the first St. Lawrence cable, of the breaks in the land line in Newfoundland. Yes, they had had their preliminary failures, all right. They had hewn out this moment from risks and difficulties. They had—

The Lord-Lieutenant was leading his people in

rousing cheers: for the Queen, for the President of the United States, for the crew of the *Agamemnon,* for the crew of the *Niagara,* for all the Wire Squadron. Then he shouted, "And let's have a cheer for Mr. Cyrus W. Field!"

Cyrus fought a lump in his throat and wished his arms were long enough to hug everybody in that crowd, from the Lord-Lieutenant down to the last little frowzy toddler, peeping out from his mother's skirts.

As the cheer died someone yelled, "Speech! Speech!" and others took up the cry.

How could he speak? How could he tell them what the moment meant to him?

"I have no words to express the feelings which fill my heart tonight—it beats with love and affection for every man, woman, and child who hears me. I may say, however, that, if ever at the other side of the waters now before us, any one of you shall present himself at my door and say that he took hand or part, even by an approving smile, in our work here today, he shall have a true American welcome. . . ."

How lame it sounds, he thought. Why can't I make them know how I feel? But the people seemed to understand. When he stopped, their cheers were louder than before. They surged forward to shake his hand. He was glad he didn't have to say anything else just then. The lump was back in his throat. The warm feeling of being one of them had wiped out the long strain and memories of bitter tirades and of taunts.

Even darkness did not drive the crowd away. They stacked a bonfire of peat, high as a two-story house, and stayed all night.

At dawn, when the last of the Wire Squadron put out from shore, the farewells were as warm, the smiles as big, the eyes as bright, as though the crowd had just arrived, and had not kept a twenty-four-hour watch to wish them godspeed.

They weighed anchor. Cyrus leaned on the taffrail, staring first at the rocky headlands, then at the thin black line disappearing into the water. He turned and stared west, across the empty expanse of ocean.

He strolled toward the paying-out machine and studied the confusion of wheels, drums, pulleys, and gears. "Anything special happening?"

Charles Bright glanced up. "I hope not."

He went to the test room. Young Professor Thomson from the University of Glasgow, who was there in Dr. Whitehouse's place, smiled at him. De Sauty, a great calm St. Bernard of a man, intent on the instrument he was watching, did not even look up.

"Anything special happening?" Cyrus asked.

"Let's hope not," De Sauty said.

Cyrus went back to the paying-out machine. Nothing to see. Just the black line running out. He went forward to the tank from which they were paying out. Half the tank men lounged around, cracking jokes. A new flake was beginning to pay out from near the core. Row after row ran off, in widening circles. The tank men glanced at it; they shifted their feet out of the way; they joked.

He went to the deck again. After an hour the engines of the *Niagara* changed their beat. He clutched the arm of a sailor. "We're slowing down! Is something wrong?"

"No-o-o. Probably getting ready to start a new flake."

"You mean we'll have to slow down the ship every time they start on another flake of cable?"

"Of course, Mr. Field. Tricky business, starting to pay out a new flake. And just one kink in the cable . . ."

The sailor must have picked up that gesture from Ben. He grinned and spread his hands, too.

After a time the engines of the *Niagara* stepped up their beat. The cable was paying out faster. The rumble of the paying-out machine grew louder.

Someone groaned, "Are we going to have to listen to that—that coffee-mill all the way?"

Others laughed. "Coffee-mill," they said, was exactly the name for it. Cyrus laughed with them. The roll of the deck beneath his feet . . . He excused himself. Some work in his cabin, he said.

By Sunday he was on deck again. All day and half the night he prowled from coffee-mill to test room, from taffrail to tank. Monday, even though a heavy swell warned that a stiff wind was coming, he kept up his endless tour.

By Monday night Charles Bright had done what no cable engineer had done before. He had paid out over three hundred miles of armored cable. He was paying it out now into water more than two and a half miles deep. Hollow-eyed from lack of sleep he stood over the coffee-mill, giving orders to the man at the brake.

Every time the stern of the *Niagara* lifted in the swell, he said, "Ease the brake." Every time the ship plunged off the crest of a wave, he nodded, and the man tightened the brake again.

Cyrus watched until he found his fingernails biting into his palms. Good Lord, would the engineer have to watch for every pitch and plunge of the cable ships from here to Newfoundland?

But of course they had to keep enough pressure on the cable to keep it from paying out too fast, or they'd run out of cable before they got across. And when the stern of the ship lifted on a swell, of course that put more strain on the cable.

Maybe an engineer can stand it, he thought, but I can't! He went to his cabin and finally slept.

Sometime before morning he wakened and sat up with a jerk. What was it? What noise had been loud enough . . . He listened. Not sound, but silence, had wakened him. The coffee-mill had stopped.

He flung on his clothes and raced to the deck. He

did not have to ask questions. The white faces, the shocked eyes, told the story. The cable hanging limp over the stern, the frayed, broken end swinging with the motion of the vessel.

By the coffee-mill one of the engineer's assistants was trying to explain between broken sobs. "We were pitching harder. I knew the next wave was going to lift us higher than ever. I meant to ease the brake! I meant to ease the strain on the cable! That's what I meant to do! I didn't mean to tighten it! You believe me, don't you? I didn't mean to tighten it!"

Over and over he pleaded. No one could answer him. They did not look at him. They stared at the water. The restless, savage Atlantic that had robbed them of almost four hundred miles of cable.

They lowered the flag to half-mast and turned back.

Chapter 11

Men Against the Atlantic

The Atlantic Telegraph Company versus The Atlantic Ocean. When Cyrus talked with the directors that was the thought that ran through his head. Men against the Atlantic. Financiers, engineers, electricians, cable men, and mariners plotting to outwit the Atlantic.

They must sell more stock and raise more capital. They must have more cable next year, so that, no matter what the Atlantic did—how much she snatched from them—they could go on.

They must have a better paying-out machine, so that no man, in a moment of excitement, could make the brakes too tight. So that, no matter what the Atlantic did, they could save the cable.

They would follow their engineer's advice, start from a mid-ocean splice, and steam in opposite directions.

They would make an earlier start next year, so that, no matter what the Atlantic did, they could wait for a favorable time to make the splice.

Men against the Atlantic. Point by point they plotted their campaign, just as a military strategist would plot. But with one difference, Cyrus knew. The enemy they plotted against was not something that threatened their nations. The people as a whole were not concerned about their campaign. In fact, the people as a whole thought they were fools to do battle again.

The admiralty was back of them. The *Agamemnon* and an escort vessel would be at their service. They must have escort ships to cruise back and forth, warning other vessels out of the path of the cable ships, to stand by with buoys in case of trouble. They must—what was it old Ben Surrey had said?—"Hope for the best and be prepared for the worst." So the *Agamemnon* and an escort would be at their service.

Would the United States be back of them, too? With the *Niagara* and an escort? Perhaps, one of the directors suggested, when Mr. Field got home, he might use his powers of persuasion? Cyrus wondered how much they had heard of the bitter debates in Congress. He promised to get right after it. He could not think of anything that would delay him.

There was quite a bit of news waiting for Cyrus when he got home after the failure to lay the cable. News of Dudley, first. For years Dudley had headed that commission to codify the laws of the state of New

York. Now other states were beginning to adopt the civil code he had helped shape. Dudley was not only "one of the most respected lawyers in New York." His name was spreading across the nation. News of Stephen, too. He was a justice on the supreme bench of California.

There was even news for Cyrus about himself. A panic was sweeping the country. His firm had suspended payment.

"We've got between three and four hundred thousand due us," his manager explained. "And if they don't pay us—well, the safest thing seemed to be to suspend payment ourselves."

"That's about as 'safe,'" Cyrus declared, "as standing still on a thin place in the ice!"

He gave notes, or goods from their warehouses, for every cent they owed. Then he set to work. He wasn't even a Sunday Father. Just a man who sent telegrams to his family and got home between trains once in a while.

By the end of November he had the paper company on even keel—he hoped. Unless the panic got worse. He went to Washington. It had taken him two months not to get any action. He wasn't sure how much longer it might take to get an answer.

By the end of December the government had promised the *Niagara* and escort for next summer, and the navy had given Lieutenant William Everett, Chief

Engineer of the *Niagara,* leave of absence to go to England immediately. They needed Mr. Everett over there. Charles Bright had some definite ideas about the new paying-out machinery. Mr. Everett was just the man to carry out those ideas, and to add a few of his own.

Cyrus and the young lieutenant rode up from Washington together. Mr. Everett was sailing on the *Persia* the sixth of January.

"When will you be in England, Mr. Field?" he asked.

"Not before May, I hope. I'd like a little time to keep an eye on my business affairs. And heaven knows I'd like some time with my family."

A letter waited for Cyrus: If humanly possible, would he come back to England at his earliest convenience? He sailed on the *Persia,* too.

In London Cyrus had a feeling that the conversation of the directors stopped in mid-sentence when he entered the meeting. The men looked at one another, and then at William Brown.

Mr. Brown pursed his lips, studied the ceiling, then explained. They wanted Cyrus to accept the position of general manager of the company, to stay in England to—well, keep things pulled together.

They knew it would mean a sacrifice, that he must neglect his own affairs to give all his time to the Atlantic Telegraph Company until the cable was laid, Mr. Brown went on. But they would try to reimburse him in part. A thousand pounds, in addition to his expenses.

"A thousand pounds? I wouldn't accept that job for twice a thousand pounds! Or for five times a thousand pounds! But—" Cyrus paused, and his glance swept every face. "But if the vote of the directors is unanimous, I'll accept the position without pay." He strode from the room.

He had scarcely closed the door behind him when there was a burst of applause and Mr. Brown and Mr. Brooking came out, smiling.

"We are to escort our general manager into the meeting!"

"You really startled us for a moment," John Brett confessed a few nights later, "when you said you wouldn't accept the position for five times a thousand pounds."

"But that I would accept it if the vote was unanimous?" Cyrus grinned. "That must have shocked the stragglers into the fold."

"But—but—just what do you mean?" Mr. Brett stammered.

"Now, Mr. Brett!" Cyrus imitated the patient tone that John Brett had used sometimes, explaining about cable. "You wanted me here to 'pull things together,' didn't you?"

"Yes, of course, and I'm sure that in time—"

"I didn't want to take time. I'm a man in a hurry, you know."

John Brett laughed with him, then gave him a paper. "Our next report to the stockholders. I marked some paragraphs for you. I thought you might like to send them to your wife."

. . .The directors cannot close their observations to the shareholders without bearing their warm and cordial testimony to the untiring zeal, talent, and energy that have been displayed on behalf of this enterprise by Mr. Cyrus W. Field of New York, to whom mainly belongs the honor of having practically developed the possibility and of having brought together the material means for carrying out the great idea of connecting Europe and America by submarine telegraph. . . .

He is now again in England, his energy and confidence in the undertaking entirely unabated; and, at the earnest request of the board, he has consented to remain in this country for the purpose of affording to the directors the benefit of his great experience and judgment as general manager of the business of the company . . .

Cyrus copied the marked paragraphs in a letter to Mary. He hoped they would help her face the long months ahead. The months when she "would have to listen to what people said, and wouldn't know how to answer back."

There was plenty being said. He knew that. Even

eminent scientists, here and in America, were saying "I told you so" in very dignified words.

Just the other day an eminent scientist had signed a statement in the London *Times*. The whole idea, he declared, was impossible. It had failed in fifty-seven. It would fail again. Failure was inevitable.

"Does that sort of talk bother you?" Cyrus asked Charles Bright.

"Oh, no! Because I don't have to answer them. But all these letters we get from people who want to help us! They're the ones that take the time!" He showed Cyrus a handful.

An officer high in the admiralty suggested that they should wind the cable on one huge drum, tow it across the Atlantic, paying it out as they went.

"Three thousand tons of cable," Mr. Bright said. "I wonder how big a drum it would take to buoy it? But of course I'll have to answer him."

Another letter, in flowery script full of curlicues, stated that Madame Zelda, clairvoyant, was ready to offer her invaluable help. For the mere pittance of ten thousand dollars she would accompany the expedition, and put her great skill at their service. In case of a break in continuity, she could divine the trouble. In case of a complete break in the cable, she could divine the exact spot where it occurred.

Charles Bright grinned and looked younger than usual for a moment. "For quite a few years I've been using an invention of my own to determine where a break was in an underground line."

"How old were you when you invented it?"

"Seventeen."

In the midst of all these offers of "help" a letter came from Professor Thomson. He had perfected an invention that would revolutionize submarine telegraphy.

"I wish I could get away right now," Charles Bright said. "I'd like to see that."

Cyrus caught the next train for Glasgow.

The young professor—he wasn't quite thirty-four yet, though he had headed a department in the University of Glasgow for twelve years—greeted Cyrus eagerly and took him straight to his laboratory.

"The problem in working the Atlantic cable," he said, "will be to send a current of electricity through more than two thousand miles of wire and receive it strong enough to work our signaling apparatus."

"If we put a lot of batteries together," Cyrus asked, "can't we get enough current?"

Mr. Thomson smiled. "Or we can have a very light signaling apparatus."

"How lightweight?"

"Let's hear you guess," Mr. Thomson suggested.

"A pound?"

Mr. Thomson laughed. "Mr. Field! Remember! We've going to have to work that apparatus from two thousand miles away!"

"A half a pound?"

Mr. Thomson shook his head.

"Only an ounce?" Cyrus asked.

"Less than a grain," Mr. Thomson said. "Not a five-hundredth part of an ounce." He pointed to a coil of wire. "There is my signaling apparatus, in the center of that coil of wire."

The coil of fine copper wire was standing on edge. In the center of it Cyrus could see a little mirror, not half an inch in diameter, hanging by a silken thread. A tiny strip of metal was fastened across the mirror.

"That bar of steel across the mirror is a magnet," Mr. Thomson said. "When I send electricity through the coil of wire, the mirror will move. Watch."

Cyrus watched the mirror, waiting for something to happen, but nothing did.

Mr. Thomson said, "There! Did you see the mirror move?"

Cyrus shook his head. "Something must have gone wrong."

"Oh, no! It's working perfectly. It moved, all right. It's a very slight movement, but it moved. It turned back and forth. If I sent Morse code through the wire you could read it in the movements of that mirror."

"How?" Cyrus asked bluntly. "If you can't even see the mirror move?" Then he started to apologize.

But Mr. Thomson beamed. "Exactly! So we must use another apparatus with the mirror to make bigger signals, easier to read."

"How much weight will you have to add?"

"Oh, I'll not add weight!" Mr. Thomson was more and more pleased with himself. "No weight at all. That would defeat the purpose!"

A foot and a half in front of the mirror he set a lamp, shaded from the mirror with a flat sheet of metal. Across the metal shield he fastened a strip of white paper. He lighted the lamp.

"Now, Mr. Field, stand over there behind the coil, and face the strip of paper."

Cyrus watched. Mr. Thomson darkened the room. Now Cyrus could see there was a tiny hole in the metal shield, and a fine beam of light shining across toward the mirror.

"Watch what happens when I send current through the coil around the mirror."

A dot of light, reflected from the mirror, moved back and forth on the strip of white paper.

"You've done it!" Cyrus yelled. "You've done it! Man, if I were a Frenchman, I'd kiss you on both cheeks! Even I could read Morse code on that—if I could read Morse code."

Mr. Thomson laughed and let light into the room again. For a moment he stood by the coil with its tiny mirror. He touched it lightly, as he would caress the face of a baby. "I think it's the answer to long ocean cables. Apparatus we can work with very little current. At the moment," he admitted, "all my brother scientists do not agree with me."

"But why not?" Cyrus was impatient. "I'd think anybody—" He remembered the night, twenty-odd years ago, when men had called Morse a crackbrained dreamer. "No, I suppose everybody can't see it yet. It may take a while for the world to decide whether you're a—I mean to decide—"

Mr. Thomson smiled. "Whether I'm a fool or a genius? We're in the same boat there, Mr. Field. The world hasn't decided yet whether you're a fool or a man of vision. I believe the consensus still is that you are a fool."

"They'll change their minds!" Cyrus declared.

"Yes. And I hope my little mirror galvanometer helps cause them to change their minds. First, I suppose I'll have to convince my fellow electricians."

"Have you showed it to Dr. Whitehouse?"

"Yes."

"What did he have to say?"

"His remarks began 'my dear boy.'"

When Cyrus heard that once again Dr. Whitehouse, their head electrician, could not go with the expedition, he wrote to Mr. Thomson, "'It's an ill wind that blows nobody good!' You'll get to use your mirror galvanometer while we're laying the cable. That will prove you're right!"

Old Ben Surrey suggested that the coilers would appreciate it if Cyrus dropped around to see them loading the *Niagara*. They were working day and night, to make up for delays. Both ships had had to be "scooped out like crabs" for more cable. Between them they would be carrying three thousand miles. Enough for any emergency.

Long before Cyrus got down to the tank where the coilers were working he could hear them singing. Thank goodness they were not singing that dirge they had sung last year. Now the rollicking tune of "Pop Goes the Weasel" echoed through the ship. As Cyrus reached the tank the men had finished a verse. They shouted with laughter.

"Give it to us again, Randy!"

Their tenor began to sing. The tune was "Pop Goes the Weasel" but the words were new:

> "Pay it out, oh, pay it out,
> As long as you are able!
> For if you put the darned brakes on—"

All the men bellowed the last line:

> "POP GOES THE CABLE!"

They saw Cyrus and hailed him cheerily. "How's that, Mr. Field?"

"It's quite a song!"

"We thought you'd like it!" They began once more:

> "Pay it out, oh, pay it out,
> As long as you are able!"

Topside again, Cyrus got beyond the sound of the song, but the words dogged him:

POP GOES THE CABLE!

Well, at least the men were in a happy, confident mood. They wouldn't be singing a thing like that if they were upset and worried.

The next time he saw the coilers the jaunty mood was gone. They were not singing now. They glared and spoke through their teeth. A paragraph in the London *Times* was rankling:

> Both the *Agamemnon* and the *Niagara* are astonishingly deep. The lower deck ports of the former are very near the water and they are being fastened and caulked before starting. But in spite of this the *Agamemnon* carries her share infinitely better than her long, black-looking rival of the United States, which is immersed very deeply indeed by her load. The *Agamemnon* draws only 26 feet, or actually one foot less than her draft at starting last year. But even at this depth she bears herself well and looks the noble ship and one that should be seaworthy in any weather. The *Niagara*, however, draws no less than 27 feet 2 inches aft, and this great draft effects a marvelous and most unpleasant change in her appearance, since it leaves her spar deck scarcely eight feet above the water's edge. In fact the main deck is actually below the water level, and if her lofty bulwarks, some nine or ten feet high, were taken away, she would appear to be almost the last vessel in the world in which it was desirable to venture across the great *Atlantic*.

Cyrus tried to joke with the coilers, to soothe their feelings, but there was no helping their black mood. Someone had cast slurs on the finest ship in the United States Navy! There was no forgiving that! He stayed around the tank quite a time. No songs. No jokes. He began to wish they'd sing anything, even "Pop Goes the Cable."

In the next week there were three fights between townsmen and sailors from the *Niagara*. The officers threw the sailors into the brig.

"Ought to be giving them medals," a lieutenant told Cyrus, "but we've got to have discipline. Hands across the sea. All that rot."

Why, oh, why had the *Times* sneered at the *Niagara?* Nothing could have caused more bad feeling. Nothing could have made it harder to "keep things pulled together."

As the date to sail drew near, and a thousand and one things must be done, and nothing got done on time, Cyrus felt as though he were trying to run a race through knee-deep mud.

It was in the midst of one of the most mud-wading days that he got word from the United States Navy. The *Susquehanna* could not serve as escort for the *Niagara*. Yellow fever had broken out on board.

Chapter 12

Another Flag at Half-Mast

BAD NEWS, CYRUS DECIDED, TRAVELS FAST. WHEN HE MET with the directors two hours later to give them the news, they greeted him with it. Had he heard that the *Niagara* had no escort?

Yes, he told them, he had heard it two hours ago. Yellow fever on the *Susquehanna*. "So, unless the admiralty can sparc another naval vessel—"

"Out of the question," one of the directors said. "It's a wonder Sir John Pakington hasn't recalled the *Gorgon*. He's chartering merchant vessels right now to carry troops to Malta."

"I know," Cyrus agreed. "We may have to use a merchant vessel for the other escort. But a naval vessel would be better."

"Better, of course! But impossible under the circumstances!"

A young naval officer brought a letter for Mr. Field.

"From Sir John Pakington," Cyrus told them as he opened the letter.

A director groaned. "There goes our only escort!"

Cyrus glanced up from the letter. "Both the *Gorgon*,

Captain Dayman commanding, and the *Valorous*, Captain Aldham commanding, will be at our service. Compliments of the admiralty."

The directors stared. "But how did Sir John know?"

"Because I told him! Good Lord, I said I heard about the *Susquehanna* two hours ago, didn't I? What did you think I'd been doing? Twiddling my thumbs?"

John Brett started laughing first. The others joined in.

No cheering crowds gathered June 10 at Plymouth where the ships were to sail on the second expedition. A few of the directors were there, looking a bit wistful because they could not have any news of the expedition until the cable was laid. How long would it be? they asked.

Six days to the mid-ocean rendezvous, Captain Hudson said, and eight days to lay the cable—if all went well. Any time after June 24 they could expect to see the *Agamemnon* steaming into Valentia.

The directors sighed. No news for two weeks! "Well," one said, "at any rate you have a beautiful day to start."

"Too calm," Captain Hudson said. "The *Agamemnon* needs a wind, so she can use sail and save her coal."

All the ships were forced to use steam to get under way. The next morning—still too calm.

Captain Hudson hailed the *Agamemnon* with an offer. The *Niagara* had coal enough in her bunkers to use steam all the way. Could she help by towing the *Agamemnon?*

The crew of the *Niagara* grinned and nudged one another. That would be something! That would be one to tell when they got home! How they had towed the *Agamemnon!*

Captain Preedy of the *Agamemnon* refused the kind offer. He could use steam for a day or two, he said. If the light breezes held, he would take the offer of a tow under consideration.

Saturday, the third day out, the *Agamemnon* got the wind she needed. She signaled the *Niagara* that she had raked out her fires and hoisted her screw. With royals and studding sails she bowled along.

"If the wind holds," a lad on the *Niagara* said regretfully, "we won't get to tow her after all."

A grizzled old tar spit to leeward. "This wind'll do more than hold."

"The barometer's falling?"

"I ha' no need to look at a wee bit glass!"

By Sunday the wind was a gale. With nothing but reefed topsails and foresail the *Agamemnon* plunged along. The crew of the *Niagara* sighed. Too bad. It would have been such fun to tow her!

Then the wind turned into the most violent storm that even old sailors had ever seen on the North Atlan-

tic. The *Agamemnon* was rolling so badly that every wave threatened to overset her. There was no joking on the *Niagara* now.

"Two thousand tons smaller, and she's carrying as much cable as we are."

"Tore out some of her coal bunkers to make more room."

"A hundred and forty tons of coal shored up on her decks."

"If that coal breaks loose . . ."

"The way she's pounding—if a cable tank gives way . . ."

Helpless, they watched the *Agamemnon,* knowing they could do nothing to save her. The storm grew more violent and they lost sight of her.

Day after day the mountainous waves pounded the *Niagara* as she fought her way toward the rendezvous. With every violent roll, with every creaking groan of her timbers, men looked at one another, the unspoken thought in their eyes: The *Agamemnon* can never take this. They reached the rendezvous and patrolled the region, waiting for the storm to end and for the other ships—if they survived—to join them.

By the twenty-third the storm had passed. First the *Gorgon,* then the *Valorous,* appeared. No, they had not seen the *Agamemnon.*

"If anyone can bring her through that storm," Captain Dayman said, "Preedy is the man." But his *if* hung in the air.

The twenty-fifth the *Agamemnon* hove in sight. The crews of the other three vessels cheered wildly. Cyrus went with the captains to congratulate Captain Preedy. The crew of the *Agamemnon* were too tired—and too busy—to spend much time on congratulations: bracing the forward deck tank—one beam had broken under it; re-coiling a hundred miles of cable from the main tank; repairing smashed electric equipment; shoring up the tons of coal that had broken loose; repairing the paying-out machine. It had broken loose, too.

By tomorrow, Charles Bright said—if they worked all night—they could make the splice and start paying out. He hoped the calm would last.

The next day the brief calm was over; even though it was June a stiff breeze brought sleet that cut their faces.

The *Agamemnon* signaled she was ready for the splice. They secured the two ships, stern to stern, with hawsers a quarter of a mile long. They carried the end of the *Niagara's* cable to the *Agamemnon*. Their boats pitched in the chop of the waves.

"They'd better make that splice fast!" an officer muttered. "Or we'll have to wait out another storm!"

Cyrus heard the man with sinking heart. He had seen the jointers work. He knew it would take the best part of two hours to make that splice.

Ben Surrey and his assistant were at their workbench, lighting their spirit lamps, laying out their tools —knives, smoothing irons, the supply of flux, solder, naphtha, and gutta-percha.

"Hurry! Hurry!" Cyrus wanted to say, but he knew they could not hurry. The splice must be perfect. A single drop of moisture from a sweaty hand, a tiny air bubble in the gutta-percha, and their work would be for nothing.

Ben's helper stripped back the insulation and fastened the two ends of the cable in vises on the workbench.

Ben leaned close to study the copper. "You've nicked the core on this end. Cut it off and strip back again."

The helper's hand moved jerkily. He dropped a tool.

"Easy does it, lad."

The helper nodded and steadied. Again he bared the copper. Ben peered at it. He dipped his hands in naphtha and held them out to dry. Cyrus knew that from now until the whole tedious process was done, no hands but the clean, dry hands of the head jointer could touch the splice.

Minutes dragged as Ben worked over the two ends of copper, filing, lapping, wrapping them with fine copper wire.

"Ready for the flux . . . now the solder." His hands moved back and forth, holding the solder above the joint, the iron below it. Carefully . . . carefully . . . The iron must not get too close to the gutta-percha beyond the splice.

The solder melted, covering the joint with a shining coat. Ben handed the solder and iron to his assistant. He ran a fingertip lightly over the joint.

"The file." He smoothed a minute roughness. Once more he dipped his hands in naphtha and held them out to dry. He touched the joint. "Ready for the gutta now."

Cyrus couldn't stand to watch any longer. He had seen that endless process as Ben applied one thin layer after another of gutta-percha, warming it, smoothing it, kneading it, cooling it. He went away and did not come back until he was sure the splice must be done.

Ben was saying, "Ready for the second layer."

After two hours that seemed like two weeks Ben said, "That's it."

Mr. Thomson came from the test room, smiling. "Continuity's okay. We're getting signals from the *Niagara* through the whole cable."

No one cheered. They were too tired to cheer. They bolted a wooden jacket around the splice to protect it, and lowered the splice into the water.

Again word from the test room. "Continuity's okay."

Cyrus and his companions returned to the *Niagara*. The coffee-mill was rumbling, paying out the necessary cable before they began to move.

Mr. Everett said, "That does it."

They signaled the *Agamemnon*. She answered.

The first mate lifted his trumpet. "Cast off the hawsers!"

The two ships saluted each other, and steamed in opposite directions, the *Agamemnon* toward Valentia, the *Niagara* toward Newfoundland.

The crew of the *Niagara* cheered:

"We're on the way!"

"If the *Agamemnon* just holds together, we'll get that cable laid."

"Showed them we could build ships, didn't we?"

"Showed them the *Niagara* could weather a storm!"

"Man, what a mess that *Agamemnon* was!"

The cheering—and jeering—had hardly settled down when there was a wild yell from the coffee-mill. "Stop her! Stop the ship! Grab the cable!"

But it was too late. Even as Cyrus turned, the broken end of the cable eluded the frantic hands grabbing at it, whipped over the taffrail and splashed into the water.

A gun boomed to warn the *Gorgon* of trouble. Cyrus went to the coffee-mill.

"Jumped the pulley," Mr. Everett said. "Before we could work it back on, it got tangled in the gear and broke."

The *Gorgon* closed in. The *Niagara* began to turn. Nothing for it now but to go back to the rendezvous for another splice.

On board the *Agamemnon* Charles Bright met them with a cold, controlled patience.

But someone muttered, "Can't you Yankees watch what you're doing?"

Mr. Everett flushed; his jaw hardened. Cyrus couldn't blame him for his anger. But he couldn't blame the crew of the *Agamemnon,* either. The storm had been bad enough for the *Niagara,* but they had not spent a week fighting for their lives.

It was sunset before they were under way once more. The whole day wasted. No cheers and jeers on the *Niagara* now. A tense watchfulness.

One man said through his teeth, "If there's another break, it won't be on the *Niagara!*"

Almost, Cyrus thought, as though he hoped there would be a break on the *Agamemnon.* Heartsick, he went to his cabin.

The next break didn't occur on the *Niagara* or the *Agamemnon* either one. Somewhere, miles from either ship, the insulation failed, and all the current leaked into the sea.

When the ships met at their rendezvous again Cyrus went with Everett and De Sauty to the *Agamemnon.* In the test room they compared logs. At exactly the same moment the electricians on both ships had recorded "Dead earth."

They stared at each other blankly. Was it impossible to lay a cable in the Atlantic? Were the soundings wrong? Were there uncharted mountain peaks of sharp rock, waiting to cut the cable? Well—nothing to do but try again.

On deck Ben and his helper laid out their tools.

"Thank heaven," Cyrus said to Captain Preedy, "we have enough cable."

"Enough cable," the captain said, "but not enough coal. Much more of this and the *Agamemnon* won't be able to reach Valentia under steam."

The captains conferred. To the problem of cable they must add the problem of the shortage of coal on the *Agamemnon.* How much longer did they dare stay out? They made their decisions:

If there was another break before they had each run one hundred miles from rendezvous they would return for one last splice.

Another thing: When the *Niagara* reached rendezvous, how long would she wait on the *Agamemnon?* After the ships lost contact they could not know what was happening to the sister ship. Eight days, they decided. That was long enough to wait.

Cyrus listened and shivered. Yes, eight days was long enough. If a ship not a hundred miles from rendezvous did not get back in eight days, that would mean she could not get back—ever.

If the cable broke after the ships had gone more than a hundred miles from rendezvous, what then? They would all return directly to Queenstown, Ireland, on the Bay of Cork. That would be the nearest place to refuel.

"If it's any use to try again," someone muttered.

They drew up the pact in writing. When the splice was done, once more they paid out the cable, cast off hawsers, saluted, and parted. The cold fog swallowed them.

Monday night and all day Tuesday the coffee-mill rumbled and the cable paid out smoothly.

About eleven Tuesday night Mr. Everett left his machine in charge of his assistant and joined Cyrus by the taffrail. "When did you have a good night's sleep?"

"I don't remember," Cyrus admitted.

"We've passed the hundred-mile limit." Mr. Everett

smiled. "Are you going to stand there all the way to Trinity Bay?"

Cyrus grinned. "All right. I'll go." He started below.

A man came from the test room. "Everything's fine," he said. "The *Agamemnon* just signaled that she's slowing down, getting ready to switch to her main coil."

Cyrus hesitated, then turned back to the taffrail. "Why do they slow down for that?" he asked.

"Same reason we slow down every time we start to pay out the next flake," Mr. Everett said. "Only more so. To have all the time possible to handle the cable smoothly, and be sure it doesn't twist and get a kink in it. The end of their deck coil is already spliced to the main coil. As the last flake runs out of the deck coil, they have to be on their toes to watch that there isn't a kink when it starts—"

Mr. De Sauty came from the test room. He spread his hands. "Dead earth."

It was all he said. All he needed to say. They knew what had happened. Trouble on the *Agamemnon* when she switched to the main coil.

Once more the gun boomed on the *Niagara*, calling her escort. Once more they turned east. Not to the rendezvous this time. It was too late for that. Back to Queenstown to refuel and try again. If the directors had the heart to try again.

Chapter 13

"Where Is the *Agamemnon?*"

"NOW," MR. EVERETT SAID WRYLY, "I GUESS YOU'LL GET some rest. Nothing else to do."

But Cyrus went to his cabin, ducked his head in cold water, mopped it off, and began writing. He did not know how much later Mr. Everett tapped and entered.

"What the devil?" the engineer asked.

"I was just collecting my thoughts. What to say to the directors. About trying again."

"This year?" Mr. Everett asked.

"Of course! We'll have time. We'll reach Queenstown by early July. A few days to reprovision, and we can be back at our rendezvous by the twentieth. The *Agamemnon* will reach Queenstown before we do. She's more than two hundred miles nearer port."

But when they anchored off Queenstown July 5, the *Agamemnon* was not there. She had not been heard from. People hammered them with questions:

Where was the *Agamemnon?*

Why had the *Niagara* deserted her?

Over and over Cyrus explained. "We did not desert the *Agamemnon!* We carried out our agreement! And that agreement was made because of the shortage of coal on the *Agamemnon!*"

Cold-eyed stares. "What happened to her?"

"We can't know until she arrives."

Bitter words through clenched teeth. "If she arrives."

"Surely she'll be here tomorrow!"

The sixth and seventh passed. The eighth and ninth. No sign of the *Agamemnon*. The muttered bitterness was louder. Some of the newspapers were outspoken. One wrote:

> We'll never know the truth of what happened to the telegraph expedition until the *Agamemnon* returns and gives us her report.

That night Cyrus could not sleep. He had grown used to being called a crackbrained dreamer, a madman, a fool. But no one had called him a villain and a coward.

The tenth passed. The eleventh. People on the street slewed sidelong glances at him as he drew near, and muttered to each other when he passed.

On July 12 guns boomed on the *Niagara* and a cheer went up. The *Agamemnon* had been sighted!

Shaking with relief Cyrus went aboard, only to face more anger and more questions:

"What the devil happened?"

"Why didn't the *Niagara* return to rendezvous?"

He spoke of the pact—that both ships had passed the hundred-mile limit. An avalanche of scorn hit him then:

"Of all the fool things!"

"To give up when we'd barely exceeded the limit!"

"What's the matter with you Yankees?"

"Don't you have any guts?"

Cyrus clenched his teeth until he could trust himself to speak. "I'm sorry. I'm desperately sorry about the misunderstanding. I wish I could say something that would help. I can't. Maybe what I say to the directors will help."

A telegram waited for him when he went ashore. The directors would meet with him as soon as he could get to London. They would meet and decide how to dispose of the cable.

No! They could not do that! He must make them see! They must not give up! Brown—he'd stand back of it. Brooking—Cyrus was sure of him. With Brown and Brooking . . .

Mr. Brown did not meet with the directors. He had sent a note:

> We must all deeply regret our misfortune in not being able to lay the cable, but I think there is nothing to be done but to dispose of what is left on the best terms we can. . . .

Cyrus looked from one face to another, and found

nothing but despair. He could not make a single pair of eyes meet his. "Mr. Brooking . . ." he said.

Mr. Brooking got up slowly. "Gentlemen, I'm sorry, but I'm resigning my position as vice-chairman of the board." He left the room.

The others must have known how that hit Cyrus. For a moment their glances did meet his. Pitying eyes. Then they studied the table again.

Mr. Thomson, their acting head electrician, reported. He urged them to try again. Mr. Bright reported. They still had enough cable to span the Atlantic. A safe thirty per cent over the distance. That was why they had ordered extra cable, wasn't it? To allow for accidents? Moreover . . .

How clearly and logically their head engineer presented his facts and figures! Surely no one could listen to him and not be convinced! Surely . . . But Cyrus remembered how clearly and logically Charles Bright had presented his arguments last year about not starting to lay the cable from Valentia. Logic had not persuaded the directors then; it was not persuading them now.

"May I say something?" Cyrus asked. He told of going aboard the *Agamemnon* when she reached Queenstown, of the scorn he had faced:

"What's the matter with you Yankees?"

"Don't you have any guts?"

"And, you know, I could sympathize with the crew

of the *Agamemnon.*" One head jerked up, then another. They were listening. "That crew had gone through more danger, had suffered more hardship, than many a crew under enemy fire. They had been without fresh food for days. They were dangerously low on coal. But they were ready to try again. They would have ripped out bulkheads and burned masts and spars to land that cable. Gentlemen, they would have broken out anchors and *kedged* that ship into Valentia Bay!"

Every man was looking at him now.

"We on the *Niagara* were living up to the agreement when we turned back. We were thinking of the coal supply of the *Agamemnon.* Perhaps we should have forgotten the coal and remembered the courage. Not long ago I was browsing through a British book. William Falconer's *Epitome of Marine Terms.* He wrote it over two hundred years ago. But a lot of what he said of the British mariners had not changed. I remember one definition. Perhaps I won't quote it exactly, but I can give you the gist of it. 'Retreat: A maneuver known to the French navy, who are expert at it. We advise that you consult them. Our comments could come only from hearsay. Retreat is not properly part of the British marine.' "

One of the directors stroked his finger thoughtfully down his thin, aristocratic nose. "A paper salesman, weren't you, Mr. Field?"

"I was."

"No wonder you made your fortune before you were thirty-five." A warm smile began on his lips and lit his eyes. "I don't see how a customer could have resisted you. I can't." He looked around the table. "Gentlemen, we cannot let the British Navy down. I suppose it's a hundred-to-one chance, but I vote we try again!"

They voted; they would try again. Just as soon as the ships could reprovision. How long would that take?

And the moment of relief Cyrus had known was gone. The pressure of time running out gripped him again. July 13 now. If they were to lay the cable before mid-August . . . and they knew that was the deadline of safety in the Atlantic . . .

Early the morning of July 17 the *Gorgon* and *Valorous* were ready to sail.

"We'll see you at the rendezvous!" Cyrus promised.

"Aye, aye, sir." The answers were polite, but unsmiling. They weighed anchor and disappeared.

That afternoon the *Niagara* hoisted the Blue Peter, and the last of her crew hurried aboard.

Cyrus went to take leave of the *Agamemnon*. "We'll see you at the rendezvous!"

"Aye, aye, sir." Polite, unsmiling, too.

The *Niagara* weighed anchor. No crowds, no cheers, no one to see her off. Even the ships she passed did not salute her. What a contrast to last year's departure from Valentia Bay. Then, almost everybody around them had believed they would succeed. Now, almost nobody believed. Not even, he knew, the crews on the ships. They had their orders. They would carry them out. But they had lost hope.

July 23, six days from Queenstown, the *Niagara* was at the rendezvous. A millpond. Not a ripple. Cyrus looked at the water and tried to remember what it had been like through the storm. *A time calm enough, a sea smooth enough* . . . They had it now!

He joined an officer at the rail. "Really calm as a millpond, isn't it?"

"Too calm." The officer looked at the streamer hanging limp from the main truck, and the dogvane that should have pointed the way of the wind. "Too calm. The *Agamemnon* needs a wind if she's not going to use too much coal getting here."

"Maybe we'll get a breeze tonight," Cyrus said.

They did not. The next day the sun climbed through empty blue. Toward afternoon a sailor pointed hopefully to a few shreds of clouds on the horizon. "Mare's-tails! That means a wind!"

Evidently they weren't mare's-tails. The streamer hung limp; the dogvane did not stir. The smoke from the *Niagara's* funnels rose straight as columns, and spread a black tent over them.

By the twenty-fifth, the second day of their wait,

the officers were keeping score of the miles Cyrus walked. Eight turns, fore and aft, they told him, was one mile. They even made suggestions about laying a carpet for his beat to save the deck.

The morning of the twenty-seventh Cyrus approached Captain Hudson. "All right if I offer a hundred dollars to the man who first sights the *Agamemnon?*"

"Think that will hurry her along? I'll pass the word."

Half a dozen of the younger lads grabbed glasses

and scampered aloft. By afternoon their wild yells were reporting the *Agamemnon* from every point of the compass.

An officer looked accusingly at Cyrus. "One more Cape Flyaway sighted, and I'll crack a couple of heads together."

Cyrus suspected that his would be one of the heads. "What's a 'Cape Flyaway'?"

"A figment of the imagination, bred by hope. Hope of a hundred dollars, this time."

On the twenty-seventh a watcher yelled, "Sail ho-o-o-o!"

There was smoke on the horizon. After a time they recognized the *Gorgon*. An hour later she was close enough for them to speak her. No, she reported, she had not seen the *Agamemnon*.

Another yell reported smoke on the horizon. The *Valorous* this time. No, she had not seen the *Agamemnon*, either.

The officers keeping score racked up two more miles for Cyrus.

At dawn the twenty-eighth, as the mist began to clear, a lookout reported, "The *Gorgon* and *Valorous* are displaying their flags! They've sighted the *Agamemnon!*"

"Ten days from Queenstown!" someone said. "Well, anyhow, she'll have plenty of coal!"

But the *Agamemnon* had fought headwinds most of

the way. She had lost time, trying to conserve her coal, and then had had to burn two hundred tons. Only three hundred tons left. Just ten days' steaming time. And she must be under steam all the way when she laid the cable.

Men against the Atlantic. Was the Atlantic going to win this battle, too? Five perfect days wasted. Now, instead of the cloudless dome of blue, a gray mist; instead of the millpond quiet, an increasing swell warned that a southeast wind was on its way. The southeast wind that would have been a godsend to the *Agamemnon* for the last ten days. Now she would have to fight it all the way to Valentia Bay.

On the *Agamemnon* they held consultation and made their agreement: If a break occurred after they had each gone 150 miles from rendezvous they would abandon the attempt and return to Ireland. No question about it this time; 150 miles was the absolute limit.

In the raw, cheerless cold they made the splice and dropped it overboard. No one spoke; no one cheered. Men did not even stand there to watch it sink. They ambled back to their stations. When they had paid out the necessary fathoms, they exchanged signals, cast off hawsers, and parted.

Cyrus went to the coffee-mill. Someone had roped it off from the rest of the deck and hung signs on the rope: No one allowed inside but engineers. Over the dynamometer that Charles Bright had invented to measure the strain on the cable, another sign: Do not talk to the engineers.

Not a bad idea, Cyrus told himself. He went to the taffrail. At least he could watch the cable run out. He wouldn't be asking it questions. Could they do it this time? How much slack were they paying out? Enough to take care of any hills and valleys on the bottom of the ocean? Too much slack—so that they would run out of cable? Were the brakes holding back enough? But not too much?

He was by the taffrail again that night when Mr. Everett straddled the rope barrier around the coffee-mill and joined him.

"You haven't been over to see us."

"I read your signs."

"Good Lord, Mr. Field! That doesn't apply to you! The general manager of the company!"

" 'General manager' doesn't mean anything now. It all depends on other people. I'm just excess baggage, really."

"If it hadn't been for our general manager," the young engineer said, "I don't believe we'd be where we are now. I can think of a substitute for each of the rest of us, but I can't think of a substitute for you."

Cyrus could feel a flush crawling to his face. "Thank you. But my work is done."

"Then why don't you get some sleep?"

"You know, I believe I will!"

A man with tar-blackened hands approached them. "Mr. Everett, will you stand by tonight? Near as we can figure it, we'll be changing from the forward spar deck coil to the coil below it about three A.M. It's always a tricky business, changing coils. A single kink in the cable—"

"Don't worry!" Mr. Everett's smile was easy. "There isn't going to be a kink in that cable."

"No?"

"Absolutely not. Because we're going to do it absolutely right."

"Thank you, sir. You'll be there?"

"Of course."

Cyrus went below and tried to sleep. But when he was sure it was almost dawn it was two o'clock. And at least two hours later it was only two-fifteen. He gave up, dressed and went topside to join the crowd of men who were looking down over the wooden wall into the forward spar deck tank. He wasn't the only one who had found he could not sleep while that operation took place.

Chapter 14

"Land Ho!"

IN THE FLARE OF THE LANTERNS CYRUS COULD SEE MR. Everett in the tank with the men. The last flake was paying out. No singing now. No joking. Turn after turn ran off.

"Only thirty more turns," Mr. Everett said quietly. "Pass the word."

The beat of the engines changed. Slower . . . slower . . . The time for the switch to the next tank was almost there. For a moment Cyrus leaned against the wooden wall and closed his eyes. A single kink in the cable—a weak splice . . .

Again Mr. Everett's quiet, confident voice. "Look out, now, men."

Cyrus opened his eyes. Two men knelt by the cone in the center.

"Last turn but one."

The men knocked one board out of the cone.

"Last turn."

As the last turn ran off men seized the cable and ran with it to the center. Others knocked the last boards of the cone out of the way. The men who held the cable straightened the bight in their hands and reached up with it. The part they had been holding snaked upward through the hatch. From below, the splice appeared, and disappeared upward. The cable paid out smoothly from the tank below.

"Hurrah!" Cyrus clapped, then stopped. He need not have worried. Everybody else was clapping, too.

The throb of the engines changed again, picking up speed. Cyrus turned, almost too tired to stand up, and stumbled back to his cabin. He went to sleep to the rumble of the coffee-mill and the throb of the engines. He wakened late the next morning to the same cheering sounds. He even smiled when he heard the tank men singing "Pop Goes the Cable."

Toward noon the overcast cleared enough for Captain Hudson to shoot the sun. A few moments later a signal gun boomed, warning the *Gorgon* of trouble, calling her to stand by. A buzz of questions ran over the ship. A buzz of rumors followed. The *Niagara* had slowed down until she barely had way on.

"We're off course," an officer told Cyrus. "If the sky hadn't cleared enough for us to get our position —well, we'd have run out of cable before we reached Trinity Bay."

"How could we get off course?"

"Because our compasses are off!"

"What can we do?"

"Let the *Gorgon* close in and lead the way. We can depend on her compasses."

An angry mutter ran over the *Niagara.* Why should the compasses on the *Gorgon* be any more dependable than those on the *Niagara?* Had the London *Times* said so?

"Stow it, you fools!" the officer bellowed. "It's the iron in the cable that's making trouble. The *Gorgon* isn't carrying cable. Thank God she's standing by! And thank God she's got one of the ablest officers in the British Navy in command!"

The muttering stopped. When the *Gorgon* took over to lead the way the crew of the *Niagara* broke rules. Without permission they manned the shrouds and gave her a cheer. Cyrus felt a knot in his chest loosen. A knot that had been there ever since the *Times* cast slurs on the *Niagara.*

August 1. At the rate they were going they would reach Trinity Bay by August 5. In four more days. But Cyrus wasn't counting the time by days, nor by hours. By minutes. It took only a minute for something to happen. Not even a minute. A second. Back and forth, from dynamometer to tank, from coffee-mill to test room, from taffrail to bow, he prowled.

The skies cleared, but the ocean seemed very rough. Never, excepting in the June storm, had the *Niagara* been so uneasy.

"Another storm brewing?" Cyrus asked Captain Hudson.

"No. The barometer's rising."

"What's giving us such a rough time of it?"

"We've been lightering our cargo at the rate of more than a hundred and fifty tons a day. Burning between thirty and forty tons of coal. Paying out more than a hundred tons of cable. A cable ship is in a precarious state when she nears the end of her run. Not enough ballast."

"Can we do anything?"

The old captain spoke quietly. "Yes, Mr. Field. We can pray to God that it doesn't get any rougher. Pray to the God whose hand can still the raging sea."

Four days from success, and they were still men against the Atlantic. Cyrus reeled and stumbled the length of the pitching deck to the taffrail and watched the cable. The black line stretched taut as a bar of iron, and with each pitch of the *Niagara* the cable lashed the water into a line of seething foam. Men against the Atlantic . . . Could they ever win?

August 3. Two hundred miles from Trinity Bay. The tank men weren't singing this morning. They were getting ready for the most difficult switch between tanks of the whole voyage, from the coil deep in the forward hold, up through the decks, and two hundred feet aft to the wardroom coil.

Mr. Everett said they'd get along all right. He had

picked the steadiest, most dependable men to hand up the bight of the cable through the hatches from the hold to the orlop deck, to the berth deck, and to the spar deck. He could depend on every man of them to handle the cable quickly and surely. He didn't say anything about the rest of the operation.

But Cyrus knew that that was the difficult part. He had heard the men talking. When the bight reached the spar deck, then the fate of the cable had to depend on one man. One man must take the loop of cable in his hands and walk two hundred feet on a platform built from the forward coil to the wheel over the wardroom coil. Henry Payne, one of the jointers, was the man who would walk that two hundred feet.

By dawn on the third men stood around on the spar deck, looking at the platform that Henry must walk, talking it over:

"A steady man, Henry."

"He'd better be."

"Ah, what's two hundred feet?"

"On a platform . . ."

"Ah, what's a platform?"

"If he trips with that bight in his hands . . . just one kink in the cable . . ."

"Ah, he's not going to trip!"

"If he falls and the cable gets tangled in the paying-out gear and snaps . . ."

"Henry's steady."

"Sure. Steady man. . . . Too bad we can't throw the brakes and stop paying out just long enough to make the switch."

"Well, we can't!"

Seven-thirty. Cyrus was on the spar deck, staring at the platform Henry must walk. He felt the changing beat of the engines. The *Niagara* was slowing down for the switch. Slower . . . slower . . . She barely had way on. She moved uneasily in the rolling swell. Cyrus grabbed something to steady himself and looked at the platform again.

Henry Payne and another man approached. Henry glanced at Cyrus, smiled, and lifted his hand in salute.

Cyrus tried to say something, but his throat was dry.

The man with Henry didn't say anything, either. He gripped Henry's shoulder. Henry swung himself up onto the platform and stood, feet apart, knees slightly bent, balancing himself, swaying with the motion of the ship.

A stir at the hatches. The man with Henry said, "Bight's coming up."

"Aye, aye!" Henry turned and faced aft.

Voices, faint at first, then louder, as the bight came up. "Watch, ho, watch!" from the dark hold; "Watch, ho, watch!" from the orlop deck; "Watch, ho, watch!" from the berth deck.

"Watch, ho, watch!" The men on the spar deck

handed the loop of cable to Henry. He started aft, paying out the cable as he walked.

Men swarmed up from the decks below and followed him. One man, watching Henry instead of where he was going, fell into a skylight. At the sound of crashing glass men jumped and gasped.

Henry didn't jump, hesitate, or glance back. He said, "Pick up the pieces," and walked on.

He reached the wheel above the wardroom coil. He straightened the bight, released it at the wheel, and the cable began to run up from below. Men clapped. A dozen pairs of hands grabbed Henry. Men carried him forward on their shoulders.

The *Niagara* picked up speed. Mr. Everett stopped by Cyrus a moment; he said nothing. He grinned, shook his head, and mopped sweat from his face.

That afternoon the *Gorgon's* signal gun boomed a warning.

"They say icebergs ahead," the signalman reported.

Icebergs in August? Were they joking? No, not joking. Soon the *Niagara* sighted them, too. Icebergs towering a hundred, two hundred feet above the water, and lying in wait, men knew, hundreds of feet below. Beautiful, with the sun shining on them. But just one iceberg, drifting across the wake of the *Niagara*, cutting across the cable before it sank to safety...

That day and night Cyrus prowled from spar deck

to berth deck, from test room to taffrail. About three in the morning he threw himself down in his clothes and slept.

The boom of a gun wakened him. No! Not more trouble now! Not another failure! He hurried topside.

"Land ho!" the lookout was yelling. "Land ho!"

From the oldest officer to the youngest midshipman the men of the *Niagara* stared west at the bold headlands. Half the men had tears running down their faces.

The *Gorgon* closed in, and Captain Dayman hailed them. No sign of the *Porcupine,* he said. She was supposed to be standing by, to pilot them into Trinity Bay. Probably had gone around to St. John's, or something of the sort. Should they fire a few rounds and see what they could rouse?

Their guns wakened echoes from the cliffs.

Cyrus, who was watching the *Gorgon,* saw men lowering her flag. What in the world? A moment later the British were running up another flag—the Stars and Stripes.

On the *Niagara* an officer said, "Ready!" And a huge Union Jack floated over the American ship. Both crews manned their shrouds and cheered.

Cyrus watched with a smile and a lump in his throat. Surely the cable would heal any breach between England and America. Surely . . . Where the devil was the *Porcupine?*

That day the officers of the *Niagara* racked up ten more miles for Cyrus. It was five that afternoon when they sighted the *Porcupine,* and after seven before Captain Otter came aboard.

"How soon can we land the cable?" Cyrus asked.

"Tomorrow, if all goes well."

Cyrus added another mile to his score. "If I had a way to go ashore, I'd go to the telegraph house and send a message."

"Quite a distance to the head of the bay, Mr. Field."

"I don't mind. I can handle a boat."

"Oh, that won't be necessary. The *Gorgon* is going to the head of the bay. She has supplies for the telegraph house."

They hailed Captain Dayman, and told him they had a man in a hurry on board.

"Going to be the first man ashore in the morning?" Captain Dayman asked.

"I want to go ashore tonight," Cyrus told him.

"But it'll be almost morning when we get to the head of the bay. And there's nothing there but the telegraph house, miles from anywhere."

"There'll be a path from the beach to the house. I'll find it all right."

"But . . ." Then Captain Dayman said, "Aye, aye, sir."

At two o'clock in the morning they set him ashore. With a lantern Cyrus found the path, and began to pick his way. He sank to his knees in marshy ooze, and stumbled over rocks. "You darned fool!" he told himself, but he went on.

He found the bleak, deserted-looking house, set in the side of a hill. No sign of life. He hammered on the door. No answer. He tried it. Unlocked. He went in.

"Ahoy the house!" Silence. He found the stairs and went to the hall above. Through an open door he heard snores. He entered. "Ahoy the house!"

A man muttered, sat up, and blinked at the lantern. "What the devil do you want?"

"I'm Cyrus Field! The cable's laid!"

"Good joke. Why don't you— Hey!" He scrambled out, grabbed the lantern and held it higher. "Hey! You *are* Cyrus Field!" He dashed down the hall, yelling, "The cable's laid! The cable's laid!"

Tousled heads appeared. Grumpy voices told him to shut up. Then they saw Cyrus and believed. They yelled. They shook hands. They pounded one another on the back. No use trying to sleep now! They'd have breakfast and then—

"First," Cyrus told them, "I want to send a message to the United States."

Soon as their telegrapher got back from St. John's, they said. They expected him around nine in the morning.

"Nine in the morning? Where's the nearest place that's open *now?*"

A good fifteen miles away, they said. And horrible road.

"Then show me where the road is."

They protested. Fifteen miles over that road was worse than fifty miles in civilized country.

"I've waited four years to send this message! I'm not going to be stopped by a little mud! Where's that road?"

Two of the young men looked at each other, smiled and shrugged. All right, they'd take him.

"Just as soon as we pull on our clothes!" one pleaded. "You'll wait that long, won't you? We don't have to go naked, do we?"

Cyrus laughed with them and waited until they dressed. The three of them plodded off through the mud together. Fifteen miles there, and fifteen miles back, but they sent the message.

When Cyrus returned to the *Gorgon* they greeted him with shouts of laughter. "If you aren't a sight!"

He looked down. "I did get my shoes muddy, didn't I?"

"Your shoes? Man, you've got mud on your hat!"

Two days later the electricians had installed their equipment in the telegraph house, and De Sauty was trying to get through to Valentia, to tell them he was ready to receive Queen Victoria's message. It was to be the first official message over the cable.

"Nothing yet?" Cyrus asked.

"Current," De Sauty said. "Very strong current. But no intelligible signals."

"Confound it, we were exchanging signals through the cable right up to the minute before we stopped to make the splice to the land end! So you suppose they're having trouble with their splice?"

"No, because we're getting current."

When Cyrus embarked on the *Niagara* for New York, almost a week after the cable had been landed, De Sauty's word was still the same. Current—very strong current from Valentia—but no intelligible signals.

Chapter 15

"Cyrus the Great"

LONG BEFORE THE "NIAGARA" CAME TO ANCHOR OFF NEW York Cyrus heard church bells, factory whistles, and booming guns. Boatloads of cheering people surrounded the ship. Reporters swarmed on board, elbowing each other to shake his hand. The cable was working! The Queen's message had come over, and the whole country was celebrating!

"If only you could have been here two days ago! The whole city turned out!"

It looked as though the whole city had turned out again, for cheering mobs lined the streets as Cyrus drove up Broadway, past buildings decorated with flags, bunting, lights, and mottos two stories high.

The smiling driver stopped his carriage long enough for Cyrus to read one of the signs:

The OLD CYRUS and the New

One
Conquered the World for Himself

The Other
The Ocean for the World

When Cyrus got home, and the hugs, kisses, and shrieks of delight had settled down to smiles and shining eyes, Mary said, "There's a little mail on your desk. Perhaps you'd like to check it before dinner?"

As he reached his desk he heard a burst of laughter from the children. The letters and telegrams would have filled a bushel basket. Mary had laid aside what she thought he would want to see first—a telegram from Newfoundland.

The directors in Valentia, De Sauty reported, had ousted Dr. Whitehouse and his huge induction coils. They had installed Mr. Thomson's mirror galvanometer, and were working the cable with only the power of a few Daniell cells. Reception was still slow, but as soon as they ironed out that situation they would open the line for business.

Good for Mr. Thomson! Cyrus thought. He left the bushel of congratulations until after dinner. Mary and the children helped him open them. It was more fun than Christmas, the children said.

Then one sighed. "If only you could have been here for the celebration!"

They soon found that the celebration on the sixteenth and seventeenth of August was a mere flash in the pan compared to the celebration that New York was going to have. The city fathers set aside Tuesday and Wednesday, the first and second of September, for "General Celebration of the Laying of the Atlantic

Cable." It would begin with a *Te Deum* at Trinity Church the morning of the first, then a parade, then a celebration at Crystal Palace, and end with a dinner on Wednesday night.

Cyrus and his family were at breakfast that Tuesday morning when a breathless messenger arrived. Could Mr. Field and his family be ready to start to the church in half an hour?

"But the service isn't till ten!"

"I know, sir, but the crush in the streets—we've never seen anything like it! If you start in half an hour you'll be there in time—we hope!"

Even with so early a start they were barely on time for the service. Everybody in New York seemed to be in the streets. After the service, the crowd had doubled. At noon, when the parade was forming at the Battery to march to Crystal Palace, it looked as though the crowd had doubled again.

A smiling man who was dashing about attending to things shouted to Cyrus, "Good thing the parade leaves here at one o'clock! We're due at Crystal Palace at four-thirty! We'll need three hours and a half to get to Forty-second Street!" They needed more time than that. It was almost six o'clock when they reached Crystal Palace. In spite of the mobs on the street, ten thousand people were waiting there to cheer the heroes and listen to the speeches. Cyrus found it hard to keep his mind on the Mayor's address:

"The city of your home delights to honor you! . . ."

"We'll get along," Father said. "In Stockbridge, we're among friends. In New York, you'll be a stranger in a strange land."

". . . your fellow-citizens, conscious that the glory of your success is reflected back upon them . . ."

Pat Kelly grinning at him. "Well, exactly what he said was, 'long, lean, red-headed and probably lost looking.' And, lad, that fitted you to a T!"

For a moment Mary caught his eye. He knew she was thinking of the same thing. When he saw her smother a giggle he knew what she was remembering, too. The other day a man on the street had pointed out Dudley and said, "That's Cyrus Field's brother."

At home that night Cyrus found a long message from Mr. De Sauty, summing up their progress to date. So far, they had exchanged four hundred messages between Newfoundland and Ireland. Two of the most important had been cables from the British Admiralty, canceling orders that were on their way by letter to recall two British regiments from Canada. Those two messages, a British officer had said, had saved the British government at least fifty thousand pounds—more than three times their annual subsidy to the cable company.

And Charles Bright, Mr. De Sauty reported, was now Sir Charles Bright, the youngest man ever knighted in England.

"Oh, Cyrus," Mary said, "you must write to him right away!"

"Write?" Cyrus laughed. "I'll send him a cable tomorrow. Even if the line isn't open to the public yet, I can send that! That comes under the head of Atlantic Telegraph Company business!"

"The cable will be open to the public soon, won't it?"

"Of course. Just any day now." He hoped he was right. Messages were stacked a foot high at the cable office, waiting to be sent. People were getting impatient. America was full of men in a hurry. If only the electricians would begin to get some speed out of the way they worked the line!

The next night six hundred guests sat down to the dinner at the Metropolitan Hotel. Cyrus picked up the bill of fare beside his plate:

MUNICIPAL DINNER
BY THE
COMMON COUNCIL OF THE CITY OF NEW YORK
TO
CYRUS W. FIELD,
AND THE OFFICERS OF
H. B. M. Steamship *Gorgon* and
U.S. Steam Frigate *Niagara*,
IN COMMEMORATION OF THE
LAYING OF THE ATLANTIC CABLE.
METROPOLITAN HOTEL, SEPTEMBER 2d, 1858.

The menu began with oysters on the half-shell, and marched through soups, fish, boiled dishes, roasts, and cold dishes, to eighteen entrées, eighteen pastries, and eighteen confectioneries.

Board and room, the landlady told him, would be two dollars a week. Yes, she admitted, two dollars a week was high, but prices were going up, and she prided herself on setting a good table.

That night when he and Mary got home they just sat and looked at each other. Finally he said, "Do you know what I'd like to do? I'd like to go to the country

—somewhere far out in the country—and raise cows. Very large, very quiet cows."

"Cyrus, darling, you mean you're really ready to slow down?"

"I wouldn't go through the last four years—almost five, isn't it?—I wouldn't go through them again for *six* Atlantic cables!" He went to his desk. "By the way, here's something I want you to read. When I reached New York I sent my report to the Atlantic Telegraph Company. They have it by now." He handed her a bulky letter. "This is a copy of it."

Mary gulped. "I'm to read all of it?"

"No, just the last paragraph." He watched her face as she was reading it, waiting for her to smile. Since his work was done, he had resigned as general manager of the Atlantic Telegraph Company.

But Mary did not smile. She only whispered, "Oh, Cyrus, thank you!" She dropped the letter, buried her face in the crook of her arm, and sobbed.

"Mary!"

"Oh, Cyrus, it's been so long and so lonesome!"

"I know. It's been lonesome for me, too."

"But you've been *doing* something. I've just had to wait . . . and wait . . . and listen to what people said! And—" She tried to stop crying.

"There, there! Get it off your chest!" He gave her his handkerchief. "Go on. Say everything that's on your mind."

She did. At last she mopped her face, and gave him

a shaky smile. "I didn't mean to do that. But that—" She whispered two words. The second word was "cable." She gasped and put her fingers over her mouth. "Oh, Cyrus!"

He laughed until he had to borrow a handkerchief himself to wipe his eyes.

The next morning they slept so late that they were dawdling over breakfast when a messenger came at noon.

A telegram from Newfoundland. They were having trouble getting through to Valentia, De Sauty reported. No intelligible message for forty-eight hours.

Chapter 16

"Charge It Off—"

No messages for forty-eight hours! BEFORE CYRUS COULD collect his spinning thoughts and decide what to tell Mary, she spoke.

"They're having trouble with the cable, aren't they? So your work isn't over. It's going to go on . . . and on . . ." The flat hopelessness in her voice was harder to stand than her tears had been.

"Please, Mary, don't get panicky! Just because they're having a little temporary trouble!" He tried to tease her. "Let's see you frown and make it stick."

He should not have said that. He knew it the minute the words were out of his mouth.

She gave him a stiff little smile that didn't belong on her face at all. "I never have frowned at you, have I? Maybe because we've never had very much time together. Maybe I didn't want to waste any of it frowning."

"Mary, I'm sorry! I don't know what made me say it. I don't know what I am saying. I'm so—"

"Cyrus!" She came to his chair and leaned her cheek against his head. "My poor darling. My poor long, lean, red-headed, lost-looking darling. Go on downtown, dear. See what you can do."

"You understand?" he pleaded. "That I can't resign now?"

"I understand. You've always run awfully fast, but I've never caught you running away from anything. And—you won't see any more tears. I promise you that."

Mary could not quite keep that promise through the next two months. Not when the people who had been calling him "Cyrus the Great" began to hint that he was a swindler—that the Atlantic cable was a hoax. Not when columnists made much of the fact that the cable had worked (so the company said) right up to the day of the big celebration. Not when they asked sly questions about how many shares of Atlantic Telegraph stock Cyrus had managed to unload before the hoax was exposed.

Day after day Cyrus read the news from Newfoundland with alternate hope and despair. Weak current received . . . nothing today . . . current today, but nothing intelligible. The end of October the final word. The cable was dead.

He read the message twice before it penetrated. He felt only a numb relief. That night for the first time in two months he slept soundly. He wakened the next morning without the knot of dread in his chest.

At breakfast with Mary he said, "I don't know what the devil makes me feel the way I do."

"You don't? I do. You're ready to charge it to profit and loss and start over."

He stared at her. "You're uncanny! You're worse than a mind reader! You can read my mind before I know what I'm thinking, myself!"

"I suppose you'll be booking your passage," was all she said. "My promise still stands. No tears. Not very many, anyhow."

In the cable station at Valentia Cyrus watched Mr. Varley, one of their electricians, demonstrate what had ruined the cable. Mr. Varley took a piece of gutta-percha-covered core, pricked the gutta-percha with a needle, then bent the wire to close the prick. He attached one end of the wire to a piece of the cable, and submerged the rest of it in a jar of sea water. He grounded the jar, so that current would flow.

"Now I'll show you what happened to the insulation when Dr. Whitehouse's huge five-foot induction coils were used, and a tremendous voltage hit the cable."

In a few moments the voltage had ruptured the gutta-percha. Current flowed through the needle-pricked spot, burning a hole half an inch long in the gutta-percha. Charred bits of the insulation floated to the top of the water.

"That," Mr. Varley said, "is what killed the cable.

Those first days, when Dr. Whitehouse was using high voltage. By the time we switched to Mr. Thomson's method—using only the mirror galvanometer and a few Daniell cells—the gutta-percha was already ruined. You might say that, before we sent the first message, the cable was already fatally ill; it took it three months to die."

When Cyrus made a hurried trip home to put his business affairs in order he told Mary of the demonstration.

"So the cable is absolutely ruined?" she asked.

"Yes. But we're not giving up! We've proved what we can do! The cable was an engineering success; we proved we could lay it in spite of the Atlantic!"

"So you'll charge it to profit and loss and start over?"

For a moment he didn't speak. Then he asked, "How about it? Can you put up with another year like this last one has been?"

"I married you 'for better or worse,' you know." She smiled. "Of course, I didn't know how 'worse' it could be." Then she sobered. "Yes, Cyrus, I'm ready for another year—or two years—or three—"

"Good heavens, woman! Don't talk about three years! One year will be bad enough!"

In the six years that followed it comforted him to remember what she had said. . . .

The months in England in '59, when they struggled

to raise money for another cable and could not raise one-fourth of it.

December of '59, when a fire burned his warehouses to the ground, and he lost $40,000 more than his insurance.

The panic of 1860, when he went bankrupt, and mortgaged everything he owned to pay off at twenty-five cents on the dollar.

The months he traveled 6,000 miles by train, steamer, open wagon, stagecoach, and fishing boat, from Quebec to St. John's, Newfoundland, to save the charters of the cable companies.

The night he talked in Boston and the solid citizens cheered him to the rafters, passed resolutions commending his vision and foresight—and walked out without subscribing one dollar.

The early days of the War Between the States, when the *Trent* affair almost led to war with England, too.

The years when more and more former friends crossed the street to keep from meeting him.

Six years of closed doors, deaf ears, and cold eyes. And Mary never said, "Why don't you give up?"

The spring of '64 he was in England again. By then he had lost track of how many times he had made the crossing. Once more he talked with Mr. Glass, of Glass and Elliot, about a cable. Glass and Elliot had combined with the Gutta-Percha Company. The new Telegraph Construction and Maintenance Company was the biggest in the world.

Yes, they could build a cable, Mr. Glass said, and guarantee it would be in perfect working order when it was laid. They would build it themselves, and lay it themselves. The price—600,000 pounds—$3,000,000. Yes, it would cost more than the cable of '58. It would be much heavier.

"We've learned a few things about cable in the last six years," Mr. Glass said. "For one thing, we need a much heavier core. Three hundred pounds of copper and four hundred pounds of gutta-percha per mile. Some of our eminent scientists used to be in favor of a lighter core. We've learned better."

Cyrus remembered the argument, seven years ago, between Dr. Whitehouse and Charles Bright. Amazing what that boy—he had seemed only a boy then—had known about submarine cable!

Sir Charles Bright—in India now—laying a cable there for the British.

"The whole cable," Mr. Glass said, "will weigh about four thousand tons. Enough weight to have sunk the whole Spanish Armada. There's just one ship in the world that can carry that cable. The *Great Eastern*. She's rated at— You started to say something, Mr. Field?"

"No, I was just remembering. Clear back in fifty-five I met Isambord Brunel. He took me to see his

Great Eastern. She was just being built. He said to me, 'There's the ship to lay your Atlantic cable.' "

"He was right. Poor Brunel. Didn't live to see his great ship launched. Died of heartbreak, I think. A man can take just so much disappointment, and then—"

"Six hundred thousand pounds?" Cyrus asked. "I'll see what we can do about it." He left the cable plant.

Died of heartbreak . . . died of heartbreak . . . A man can take just so much disappointment . . .

"Pull yourself together!" he muttered. "Start *thinking!*"

He talked to Thomas Brassey, the greatest builder of railroads in the world. Mr. Brassey pummeled him with questions for what seemed like hours. At last he said, "Yes, Mr. Field. I'll put up a tenth of the capital."

Cyrus didn't say, "Good! I'll have ten men in jig time! Ten? I'll probably have twenty." No . . . that was a long time ago. He said, "Thank you! You'll hear from me."

At the hotel where he was staying they began to call him "the man who never slept." Day after day, night after night . . .

But at last he had to go back to Mr. Glass and report. "I'm sorry. We can't raise enough this year. Perhaps next year."

How much had he raised? Only 285,000 pounds, Cyrus told him. Not quite half the price.

"Sorry, Mr. Field."

"I know. So am I." Cyrus left the cable plant again.

Died of heartbreak . . . died of heartbreak . . . A man can take just so much disappointment . . .

"Shut up and start thinking!" he muttered. "How are you going to talk to the directors?"

He was with the directors, trying to persuade them that maybe, in another year . . . when Mr. Glass came to see them.

His company, Mr. Glass said, had a proposition. Suppose they accepted the balance of the cost of the cable in shares of Atlantic Telegraph Company stock?

And from Daniel Gooch, Chairman of the Board that now owned the *Great Eastern*—the "bad-luck ship" had already driven more than one company into bankruptcy—came an equally princely offer: the *Great Eastern* would lay the cable successfully, or there would be no charge for using her.

That night once more Cyrus didn't sleep. But this time he smiled as he dashed off one letter after another. To Matthew, to tell him that his long-ago work in Newfoundland would soon bear fruit. To Stephen, now a member of the United States Supreme Court. To Dudley, to Mary . . . When he had written more than a dozen, he wrote to President Lincoln:

. . . Even though our war-torn nation has not had the time and heart to concern itself much with the cable, I remember with deep appreciation my talks with you. It has helped to know I have worked with your blessing.

I pray God every night that the next dispatches from America will tell that the war is over.

It will be a very special pleasure to me that the first official message from America over the cable will come from you.

It took time for news of Appomattox to reach England. Time, too, for another dispatch a few days later, telling of the assassination of Abraham Lincoln. That night Cyrus tried to write letters and could not.

Sunday, July 23, 1865—more than eleven years since his first trip to Newfoundland—Cyrus stood on the *Great Eastern,* watching one more cable pay out into the sea, as the coast of Ireland dipped below the horizon.

Daniel Gooch joined him. "What's the matter, Mr. Field? I'd think you'd be dancing a jig. But you look —well, 'lost' is the only word I can think of."

Lost? Yes, that was the word for it. Lost on the huge ship, an eighth of a mile long. The only American among the five hundred men on board. Lost among strangers. How few of the men he knew. Captain Anderson, Canning, De Sauty, Thomson, Varley . . . he could count them all on his two hands. Thinking of friends who were dead—John Brett, Captain Hudson, Isambord Brunel. Abraham Lincoln—he had been a friend, too.

He forced a smile to answer Daniel Gooch. "Oh, no! Not feeling lost! Just—just interested. Amazing ship, the *Great Eastern.*"

Mr. Gooch's eyes were quizzical. He ambled off.

After a while Mr. Thomson and Mr. Varley joined Cyrus.

"The three black sheep," Mr. Varley said.

That's right, Cyrus thought. They must be feeling a little lost, too. Nothing to do until the cable company turned over the line to them in Newfoundland. The whole responsibility—and consequently the whole say-so—belonged to Mr. Glass's company.

The three of them wandered the endless corridors, and sat briefly in the huge, empty saloons. A mere five hundred people really rattled around in a ship built to carry four thousand passengers. They returned to the deck.

The *Great Eastern* was sailing in the teeth of westerly winds, but that did not bother her. Going against a headwind she was steady as a rock. Her escort ships, the *Sphinx*, and the *Terrible,* wallowed.

Daniel Gooch asked Captain Anderson how he was liking "land duty." The captain smiled and said in his quiet way he was liking it fine. He hoped he had "land duty" all the way across.

Cyrus did not find it quite that smooth, but he did get over "some paper work in his cabin" more quickly than usual. The next day he was on deck again.

Paying out perfectly, Mr. Canning reported. Perfect

signals, Mr. De Sauty reported. Mr. Thomson looked at the other black sheep and sighed. Perfect signals through his mirror galvanometer, but he was not in charge of it.

Mr. Varley had just suggested they might hunt up a fourth for whist when the gong from the test room signaled trouble. Every man within earshot stood motionless, listening as the engines slowed down. When the signal gun of the *Great Eastern* called her escorts to stand by, every man not on duty scrambled topside.

Canning went into the test room, and came out again. The three black sheep cast agonized looks at the closed door, but they did not ask to enter. They had no say until the cable was landed.

De Sauty came out and beckoned to them. "I know the rules," he said. "That you answer nothing unless I ask you in writing, and that you must reply in writing. But I'm not asking you. Just showing you. Come on in."

Cyrus followed the electricians into the darkened room. Thomson looked down at the dot of light on the strip of white paper.

"Swinging too far, isn't it?" he said. "There's a flaw in the insulation. Not dead earth—current is still coming through—but a flaw."

De Sauty nodded. "It might continue to work. But we're not going to risk it. We're going to pick up back to the flaw, cut it out, and splice again."

The three black sheep went on deck to watch the preparations for the picking up. In the bow of the ship two little donkey engines were getting up steam. An eighth of a mile away, over the stern, the cable still paid out. They could not stop it until they were ready to cut it. The *Sphinx* and the *Terrible* were standing by. Men with hawsers, stoppers, buoys, and chains swarmed over the side of the *Great Eastern.*

The men at the donkey engines signaled they were ready. They cut the cable, and began to creep forward with it, over the wheelhouse of one of the paddle wheels. The *Great Eastern* began to turn. When the cable reached the bow, she must be facing east, to put no more strain than had to be on the cable.

The picking up began. Mr. Canning watched the dynamometer. A double strain on the cable now. The weight of two thousand fathoms dragging one way, the picking-up gear pulling the other way. One mile an hour was as fast as they dared to pick up.

They had picked up ten miles when De Sauty signaled from the test room, "Okay now." The flaw was out of the water.

Mr. Canning watched as the cable came up, running his fingers over it, hunting for the flaw. He found it. A needle-like sliver of metal sticking into the cable. Evidently it had punctured the gutta-percha and touched the core. A needle prick—a needle-thin path for the current to escape.

Tuesday night they were under way again. The needle prick had cost them thirty-seven hours.

But once more all went perfectly. From London they received bulletins of what was going on in Europe. De Sauty posted the bulletins outside the test room. As they went farther and farther west men laughed over the time marked on the bulletins. With the difference in time zones they were reading bulletins at eight o'clock in the morning that were dated 10 A.M. from London.

"Lor'," one said, "we know things before they happen!"

The artists and journalists on the *Great Eastern* published a newspaper. They celebrated the accident to the cable with a poem almost as long as the delay. Men started singing two of the verses:

Under the sea, under the sea! Here's what De Sauty is saying to me!
Such testing as this is the perfectest bliss is!
Insulation is coming! It's strong!
So we'll test, test, test, with coils and rheometers, keys, galvanometers!
Test, test, test! Test each minute, all night and day long!

CHORUS:

Copper and zinc, acid and stink! Tink-a-tank, tink-a-tank, tink-a-tank, tink!
Copper and zinc, acid and stink! Success to the con-tin-u-i-ty!

Up from the sea, up from the sea, coy little coiler, come
hither to me!
Come Clifford and Canning, pick-up tackle manning, and
haul up that cable to me!
Mind dynamometers, hang galvanometers!
Haul, haul, haul! That fault from the depths of the sea!

CHORUS:

Rises and sinks, rises and sinks, coilings and kinks!
Long life to our copper and acids and zincs!
As long as man's able we'll stick to our cable,
And splice him and test him again!

The tank men picked up the first chorus. It had a good beat, they said. Ever so often, day or night, they bellowed cheerily:

Copper and zinc, acid and stink! Tink-a-tank, tink-a-tank,
tink-a-tank, tink! . . .

Five perfect days. Then once more the gong, buzzers, and guns signaled trouble. Once more they stopped and went through the tense and tedious hours of picking up the cable. This time the flaw was not caused by a needle-like sliver. A sturdy piece of metal was stabbed into the cable. Mr. Canning stared at it, the color draining from his face. He ordered the flawed length of cable stowed away under lock and key.

They spliced the cable; they got under way again. Continuity okay, De Sauty reported. Paying out okay, they reported from the stern. But every time Canning moved about the ship the sight of his white face left a silence in his wake.

Time and again in the next twenty-four hours Canning and De Sauty conferred. Then Mr. Canning asked that both watches of the tank men remain at the tank when the watch changed. He went there to talk to them.

"Most of you have known me a long time. You've been with me on many cable-laying expeditions. Every one of you was hand-picked for this expedition. The most dependable men we could find." He showed them the sliver of metal. "This is what was in that cable. I had to use both hands on the pliers to pull it out. I've tried to drive a similar piece of metal into the cable by any accidental means. Stepping on it with the heel of my shoe—setting the leg of a wooden stool on it. But I could not drive it in. Not unless I took a hammer and pounded it in! I'm . . ." His lips trembled. He stood a moment, fighting for control. "I'm putting it up to you. What do you say?"

"Plain as the nose on your face!" one shouted. "We've got a traitor among us!"

One of the younger tank men was bewildered. What good would it do a man to ruin the cable? What'd he get out of it?

An older man enlightened him. When the trouble with the cable was reported back in London, that would drive down the price of shares in the Atlantic

Telegraph Company. Men could buy when the price was down, and make a killing when the price went up again.

"What'd a traitor get out of ruining the cable? Plenty! If financiers put him up to it, they'll pay him a pretty penny!"

"Only he won't get away with it, Mr. Canning!" one man said. "We'll find him! And when we do, we'll keelhaul him! Just tell us one thing! Which watch was on duty when it happened?"

"It's happened twice, you know," Mr. Canning said. "The fine sliver once, this heavier sliver the second time. Once on the starboard watch, once on the port watch. So—if there is a traitor among us—there is more than one. Please, you've got to help me! What do we do?"

Chapter 17

"—And Start Again"

"PLEASE," MR. CANNING SAID AGAIN, "WHAT DO WE DO?"

The suggestion came from the tank men. Mr. Canning should station gentlemen in the tanks to watch with eyes of hawks and catch the traitors.

If they had not made the suggestion themselves, Cyrus thought, the situation would have been even worse. It was bad enough now.

When he, the only American on board, went down into the tank for his first turn as watchdog, he spoke to the men. "Please understand! I'm not here to catch one of you being a traitor. I'm here to prove there isn't a traitor among you. Do you understand?"

They cheered. They began to sing. Some of them had been coilers from the Atlantic Telegraph Company on the *Niagara* in '57 and '58. They sang "Pop Goes the Cable." After all, Mr. Field had said it was quite a song, hadn't he? After a while Cyrus asked for "Lost—Lost." They were glad to oblige. Quite a song, too, wasn't it? Had a good beat. Yes, he said, quite a song.

He was watchdog again on Wednesday morning when he heard a grating sound and a man yelled, "There goes a sliver!"

They tried to warn Canning in time, but they could not. Before the engines of the *Great Eastern* slowed down they heard the gong from the test room. Another flaw had gone into the sea. Before they could be ready to cut the cable and begin picking up, another ten miles would have run out. Ten miles they would have to reel in again, one mile an hour.

"I can tell you one thing!" Cyrus declared when he went on deck. "No man in that tank drove a spike into that cable! I'll stake my life on that!"

Then how could it have happened?

After a time Canning's face brightened. "The cable itself!" he said. "Tons of weight pressing down on each flake! That's it! That must be it! A sliver of metal dropped into the tank by accident—and the weight of the cable drove it in!"

In spite of the long, tense hours of the picking up that were ahead of him, he smiled. "Not murder, gentlemen! Just suicide!"

Once more they began the tedious process. They were getting along all right—but slowly—when one donkey engine wheezed, puffed, and gave out. They'd have to get up more steam. They stopped hauling in, and began to work over the engine.

Noon came. Captain Moriarty, their navigator, shot the sun. Two thirds of the way across!

The men who were not on duty went down to lunch.

Not Captain Anderson. He would not leave his post until the cable was paying out again.

A stiff breeze sprang up and hit the towering height of the *Great Eastern* broadside, driving her to leeward athwart the motionless cable. One of her hawse pipes began to chafe it. Men worked with frantic speed in three directions at once—maneuvering the *Great Eastern*, easing the cable as much as they dared, and—with prayerful curses—over the donkey engine. But the damage had been done. When they started hauling in again the chafed spot snapped. The broken end of the cable hit the water and disappeared. It would be a long time before it reached bottom. They were over a depth of more than two miles. The Atlantic had won again.

Except that Mr. Canning would not give up. "I'm going to grapple for it!"

Captain Anderson's eyes widened. "In this depth?"

"Yes! I've got wire rope long enough to reach it, and grapnels big enough to grab it!"

Captain Anderson shook hands. "At your service."

They took a position to windward of the line of the sunken cable, and paid out their wire rope. After two hours, Mr. Canning said, "It's on the bottom."

The *Great Eastern,* with the power of her engines cut off, started a slow drift athwart the line of the cable. Hour . . . after hour . . .

Toward morning, "We've got it!" Slowly they began

hauling in. A quarter mile—a half mile—three fourths—and a swivel snapped. The cable sank to the bottom again, taking two miles of their wire rope with it.

"Break out some more rope! Bend on another grapnel! We'll get it this time! Let's go!"

But the Atlantic said "No." Said it with a fog that closed down. For five days the three ships circled blindly, waiting for the fog to lift. Day and night their foghorns blew, and their signal guns boomed.

After five days the fog cleared. They grappled, caught the cable again, and lost it—and more rope—when another swivel snapped.

Nine days after they lost the cable Mr. Canning lowered the last rope he had.

Cyrus did not watch that last hopeless grappling. He went below to the grand saloon, brought a stack of paper to a table, and began to write.

Presently one of Canning's men came in. "We lost it. The last bit of tackle on board."

Cyrus nodded. "Thank you for coming to tell me." He reread a sentence, then stared off into space.

"Is that all you have to say?"

Cyrus glanced up. "But what is there to say?"

The man glared for a moment, then said, "Is it too much to ask what you're writing?"

"A prospectus to present to the directors when we get back to London. We've got to start making plans for next year."

"Well, I'll be . . ."

Cyrus did not hear the rest of it. He was writing.

After a while Daniel Gooch came in. "I hear you're making plans?"

"Of course."

"Good Lord, Cyrus Field! When will you give up?"

"I won't. Not till that cable is laid and working."

Mr. Gooch sighed, sat down heavily, and stared at the floor. Poor devil, Cyrus thought, he took a chance and lost. The *Great Eastern* was to lay the cable successfully, or there was to be no charge.

At last Mr. Gooch looked up. "You really think you can raise money for another cable? Another three million dollars? Man, what could you say to anybody to make him invest in a cable now?"

"That's what I'm working on."

Mr. Gooch shook his head, then got up and came to the table. He held out his hand. "Personally, I think you're crazy. But if you can raise the money for another cable, you'll have the *Great Eastern* on the same terms. No charge, unless we succeed."

They shook hands on it.

"And there's something else I'd like you to think about," Cyrus told him. "Your terms for raising this cable we just lost."

"What! To try to raise a cable after it's been on the bottom of the ocean for a year? It'll be sunk so deep in the ooze you'll never find it—let alone raise it!"

"I believe with strong enough grappling equipment we can do it. After all, three million dollars' worth of cable—it's worth a try, isn't it? And there's no doubt that we'll have plenty of traffic for two cables. So, think about it, will you? What you'll charge to do a little deep-sea fishing next summer, after we've laid the cable of sixty-six."

Mr. Gooch started to shake his head, then he shrugged and smiled. "All right. I'm crazy, too. The *Great Eastern* will go on the fishing expedition on the same terms. No charge, unless she raises the cable. But, mind you! I'm not saying the cable will be in working order! If we bring it up, you'll pay through the nose, even if that cable's dead as a dodo!"

They shook hands on that, too.

Back in London, it took longer to convince the directors. But at last they agreed with Cyrus: His plan for raising the money with twelve per cent preference shares ought to do it. They'd get right after it. Maybe . . . just maybe . . . this time they'd succeed!

Cyrus boarded the ship for home head up, and smiling. But the last night out from New York he found himself pacing the deck, unable to sleep. How would Mary and the children react to this last failure and another try?

Children—what a way to think of them. The girls were young ladies now. Alice and Gracie both older than Mary had been on their wedding day. The boys

. . . he had to count back. Eddie was born the summer the first St. Lawrence cable failed, so he was ten. Willie was born the spring before the first Atlantic cable failed, so he was eight. What a life he'd given them.

Mary, bless her, had tried to make it up to them, to make them believe in their father. He remembered once seeing her show the boys the scrapbook of clippings from '58—those brief weeks when he was "Cyrus the Great."

At home, after the first loving greetings, a silence fell, and their eyes asked questions.

"We'll do it next summer!" he said.

He saw the masks settle on the girls' faces, saw them start to speak, then stop.

Mary smiled—at least her lips did. "Of course you will, dear! And we're going to be the proudest, happiest family in the world!"

Fanny exploded. "You know what I wish? I wish all the cables in the world were on the bottom of the ocean!"

Cyrus grinned. "So do I. Especially the cable we'll lay next summer."

"Oh, you!" But she hugged him, then burrowed her head against his shoulder, and finally reached for his handkerchief.

"There, there!" he said. "Now, let's forget all about the cable! We'll have Christmas together, and New

Year's, and Valentine's Day, and Easter! I left everything in apple-pie order in England. I shouldn't have to go back before June!"

In December a hurry call from the directors took him back to London. Everything was at a complete standstill. Not a chance of doing anything about the cable this coming summer. The Attorney-General had said they could not issue the new shares on the terms they had planned—not unless Parliament passed an act legalizing the issue.

"And that," one director said, "would take at least a year. So we've done the only thing left to do. We've canceled the order for the cable, and returned the money already subscribed."

"*You what?*"

"It's the only thing we could do! We can't go against the ruling of the Attorney-General!"

"Of course not," Cyrus agreed. "We've got to find another solution. And we'll find it!"

The directors looked more cheerful as the meeting broke up. Cyrus was glad someone looked more cheerful than he felt.

Chapter 18

Friday the Thirteenth

ONCE MORE THE HOTEL STAFF CALLED CYRUS "THE MAN who never slept." Servants who went to waken him with early morning tea reported they found him already awake, either at his desk writing, or pacing the floor.

Once a maid said, "Ah, the poor man! At his desk he was, and his head in his hands. He looked at me dazed-like, and said, 'Is it morning?' He's fair disheartened."

But no one else saw him with his head in his hands or "fair disheartened." He talked so confidently of the cable they'd lay that summer that men began to hope again. Captain Anderson wrote to him:

> . . . I feel as though our watch had got the mainspring replaced, and had been trying to get along without it for the last three months. At all events, I know nothing will be left undone that human energy can accomplish.

I only hope, Cyrus thought, that human energy can accomplish it! But how can human energy overcome that edict of the Attorney-General?

He talked with John Lloyd, an outstanding lawyer. What about a new company to lay the cable of '66? Yes, Mr. Lloyd said, that should take care of things. No reason why a group of men with the money to do it couldn't get together and organize a company to lay a cable.

A group of men with money—and faith. But could he find men with faith in a project that had failed for nine years? Day after day, night after night, one interview after another. The matter of getting the backers crawled, and the days flew. January passed; February began. Not half the backers he needed.

What's the matter with you? Cyrus asked himself. Where's your drive? He knew where his drive was if he wanted to look back on the past twelve years. But he must not look back.

There came a night when he returned to the hotel after midnight, ready for once to admit defeat. A letter waited from Mackay in Newfoundland. If there was any prospect of an Atlantic cable this summer, Mr. Mackay wrote, they'd better get to work on the Newfoundland lines:

> . . . I've been holding the land lines together with prayers, perspiration, and pennies. But the St. Lawrence cable is broken. I can't mend it with prayers, perspiration, and pennies. It's going to take dollars! Quite a few!

When a maid brought Cyrus early tea she found him at his desk. A confusion of papers overflowed the desk to the floor.

"Mr. Field?"

He stared at her, bemused. "Morning?"

"You must be a bloomin' author, sir. You've fair written a book."

"This? Oh, no! Just a letter. It takes a long time to write a short letter. Did you know that?"

The maid went back to the kitchen, shaking her head. " 'Twon't be long now. If you ask me, the poor man's daft!"

The letter, when Cyrus pulled it together, was not

long. Just a few pages to his partners in New York, pleading with them to bend every effort to restore the lines in Newfoundland. This summer there would be a successful Atlantic cable! They must be ready for it!

When he had finished he folded the sheets and sealed them ready to mail. He dumped the rest of the paper into the wastebasket. He noticed the tea. When had that come? It was cold, but he drank it anyhow.

He stood up, stretched, and threw back his shoulders. What he had written to New York was true! They *would* lay a cable this summer! He began to go over his appointments for that day, planning how he would talk to each man.

By mid-March the Anglo-American Telegraph Company was a fact, the capital raised, and once more the wheels could begin to turn. They could reorder the cable for '66, and the grappling equipment to raise the cable of '65. They could . . .

Cyrus looked at the calendar. Just five months until mid-August. That was the deadline. Even at seasons when men hoped for calm days on the North Atlantic they could face storms. After mid-August they did not even hope.

Five months. More than 2,000 miles of cable to make. Five months, and the double task ahead. Four months would be the deadline for starting from Ireland. Could they do it?

Just four months later, Thursday evening, July 12, the *Great Eastern* stood off the Irish coast, and Captain Anderson announced that they would sail in the morning.

The crew stared at one another aghast. Cyrus heard their worried mutters:

"Friday the thirteenth!"

"They're crazy!"

"Haven't they had enough bad luck with their bloomin' cables without sailin' on Friday the thirteenth?"

Pipes shrilled, calling all hands on deck. Captain Anderson spoke to them.

"I've chosen the date for departure," he said, "for a particular reason. I wish to approach the Newfoundland coast at the time of the full moon. We shall hold to a steady five knots for the crossing. We shall reach Newfoundland on the twenty-seventh. We shall have a full moon."

No "if's," no "barring accidents," no "I hope's"; just the flat statement. "We shall reach Newfoundland on the twenty-seventh."

Reluctant smiles from the crew. That one! He had his nerve! But Friday rain sheeted down, and the muttering began again. Surely they could lay over one day? Just till midnight? So it would be the fourteenth?

The *Great Eastern* sailed. Three ships in her escort now. The *Terrible* standing off the starboard bow, the

Medway off the port bow, and the *Albany* on the starboard quarter, with ropes, buoys, stoppers, and grapnels.

They had "hoped for the best and prepared for the worst." They were ready for any emergency. They had taken precautions against every type of accident that had ever happened in the laying of an Atlantic cable. This time they would not fail!

After the storm on Friday they had four days of such millpond quiet that they could see the spars of their escorts reflected in the water.

When Cyrus returned to the deck after "some work in his cabin" he found Mr. Thomson at the taffrail staring wistfully at nothing.

"Just two black sheep this year," the young professor said.

Varley was at the telegraph house in Valentia, keeping watch with Mr. Glass. Willoughby Smith, long-time head electrician of the Gutta-Percha Company, was in charge of the test room on the *Great Eastern.* The test room, where Mr. Thomson's beautiful, sensitive, delicate mirror galvanometer was working its magic. And he wasn't there.

"Nice weather, isn't it?" Cyrus offered lamely. Then he thought of something brighter to say. "I wonder if the Atlantic has signed a peace treaty with us, or has just declared an armistice?"

Evidently an armistice, and it ended on Tuesday.

A storm howled through the rigging, rain hammered the decks, and waves thundered against the *Great Eastern.* For a while they could see their escort ships pitching and pounding. Then it rained harder and hid them from view.

At midnight it was too noisy to hear the engines change their beat, but every man on the ship felt it happen when they stopped and reversed.

Word flew over the ship. "A tangle in the after tank!"

Cyrus had not realized he had moved until he found himself by the huge after tank. The flake that was paying out had gotten tangled into the flake below, dragging two turns from the outer edge and five turns from the center—at least a hundred fathoms of cable—into a hopeless snarl.

As Cyrus reached the deck he heard the signal guns calling for help. Heedless of the rain he made his way aft. The cable had not parted—yet. Men were securing it with rope stoppers near the grooved wheel. Others stood by, ready to let go buoys.

Captain Anderson was at the taffrail, trying to see down into the water, watching the cable, giving orders to his engineers. Forward . . . reverse . . . forward . . . reverse . . . disconnect the port paddle wheel . . .

Where were the escorts? Why hadn't they answered the distress signals from the *Great Eastern?* Again the guns boomed, but the roar of the storm swallowed the sound.

No help for the *Great Eastern.* No hope, unless one man, staring down into the darkness over the taffrail, could keep the storm-pounded ship from snapping the cable.

After two hours they signaled from the tank, "All clear." From the test room, "Continuity okay." The paying out began again. For the first time Cyrus realized he was soaked to the skin and his teeth were chattering. Even after he was warm and dry and in his berth his teeth still chattered.

Sunday they passed the longitude of the Atlantic's last victory—where the end of the broken cable of '65 had gone down.

Monday Willoughby Smith sent for Cyrus to come

to the test room. "I thought maybe you'd like to send a message to Mr. Glass at Valentia? Ask him to gather some late news for you to have when we land at Heart's Content?"

Cyrus thanked him and worded the message, and watched Mr. Smith send it. Just eight minutes later they had Mr. Glass's answer from Valentia:

YOUR MESSAGE RECEIVED AND IS IN LONDON BY NOW.

Cyrus shivered. "Even though I keep telling men it's possible, it's still unbelievable."

"It's taken a lot of believing to make it happen, hasn't it? Years when believing has been rather a lonely business, maybe?"

For a moment Cyrus let himself remember some things he generally managed to forget. He shrugged off the thoughts and spoke quickly. "You electricians really have your hands full, don't you?"

But Mr. Smith was not going to be sidetracked from his train of thought. "Ever read the Book of Job, Mr. Field?"

"Of course. There's one verse that's lifted my spirits a lot of times." And Cyrus quoted:

> "Canst thou send lightnings that they may go, and say unto thee, Here we are?"

"I'd think," Mr. Smith remarked dryly, "that some other spots in the story of Job might stick in your head."

Cyrus smiled. "Ever see anything to beat the way we're running exactly on time?"

Mr. Smith studied him for a moment, then smiled, too. "Right, Mr. Field. Exactly on time. We'll have our full moon over Newfoundland."

They did not have their full moon. The stars in their courses said there would be a full moon. But the Atlantic said "No." A fog closed down, swallowing the convoy. They could not see half the length of the *Great Eastern*, let alone seeing the other ships. For four days and nights their foghorns never stopped: two blasts from the *Terrible*, three from the *Medway*, four from the *Albany*, and one long shriek from the *Great Eastern*.

Then, as though to welcome them, the fog lifted, and Trinity Bay lay before them.

Captain Anderson, with a straight face but twinkling eyes, suggested that perhaps Mr. Field would like to go ashore immediately to send dispatches to the United States?

Long before the ships were done maneuvering to their anchorage Cyrus burst into the cable station, pumped Mr. Mackay's hand, and waved his dispatches. "Late news for the United States!"

Mr. Mackay's smile stiffened on his face. "But didn't you know, Mr. Field? The St. Lawrence cable—it's still broken."

Chapter 19

Time Running Out

The St. Lawrence cable still broken. . . . CYRUS clenched his teeth until his jaws ached.

"Mr. Field, I've tried!" Mackay pleaded. "If I could have done it, I'd have raised that cable with my bare hands, and spliced it with my teeth! I wrote them. I begged them. I tried to make them see. But I guess . . . well, they've been pouring money into this Newfoundland line for ten years without any return."

When Cyrus could trust himself to speak he said, "Is there a steamer near that we can charter to repair the cable?"

"The *Bloodhound* is at St. John's. She could handle it."

"Then telegraph! Get her instantly!"

"Yes, sir!

"How have you been sending messages from Port aux Basques to Cape Breton?"

"We haven't."

Once more Cyrus took his time before he spoke. "Is there another steamer we can charter to carry dispatches across the Gulf?"

"I think so. A little steamer called the *Dauntless*."

"Then get her, too. And maybe . . ." In spite of anything he could do his voice was harsh. "Maybe if we can't get word to New York in two minutes we can do it in two days!"

Mackay flushed. "After we have the *Dauntless* making the run across the Gulf, sir, we'll get news to New York in twenty-four hours. In one day, sir. Not two."

"Good Lord, boy, I know it's not your fault! Nobody's fault, I suppose. Ten years *is* a long time."

Mackay relaxed and smiled briefly. "You ought to know, Mr. Field. How about it? Is thirteen years a long time, too?"

"Sometimes. Well . . . that's that." Cyrus looked at the messages he had ready to send to New York. "Get them there when you can, will you?"

He went back to the boat that waited to return him to the *Great Eastern*. A nice little job he faced now. Telling the men who could talk to Ireland in seconds that he didn't know when their messages would reach New York!

The men on the *Great Eastern* said nothing—eloquently. One finally suggested, "It'll take us quite a while to coal. Perhaps we'll have word from New York before we sail again."

They went back to their work. Every man had something to do. When they had landed the cable of '66, and had it in working order, then they must get ready for the far harder task—to bring up the broken end of the cable of '65.

Coal—five shiploads—had arrived from Cardiff. Now it was thundering into the bunkers of the *Albany* and the *Terrible.* They would leave first for the rendezvous.

On the *Great Eastern* the jointers made one last splice, joining the deep-sea cable to the land end. Communication was complete from St. John's to Valentia, and from Valentia through the vast network of telegraph lines all over Europe, under the Mediterranean, through the Red Sea, and on to India. Congratulations began to pour in—from London, Paris, Hamburg, from Berlin and Rome. But not from New York. New York didn't know about it yet. Every time men brought Cyrus another message—from Europe—he found it harder to smile.

Tuesday they got their first word from New York:

YOUR MESSAGE OF THE 27th RECEIVED SUNDAY MORNING. . . .

Forty-eight hours to get word to New York!

Wednesday, August 1, the *Albany* and the *Terrible* were ready to weigh anchor for the ocean rendezvous, to begin grappling for the cable of '65. Their captains came to the *Great Eastern* for a final conference with Captain Anderson. As they left, they shook hands with Cyrus. Perhaps, one suggested, before the *Great Eastern* finished coaling, he'd be getting quicker word from New York.

I know now, Cyrus thought, exactly what Mackay meant! I'd like to wrench that St. Lawrence cable from the ocean bed with my bare hands, and splice it with my teeth! But he smiled, thanked them for their good wishes, and went to talk to one of the officers on the *Great Eastern.* How long before they'd weigh anchor? A day? Two days?

At least a week, the officer said. Refueling the *Great Eastern* was like supplying a small city. Did Mr. Field have any idea how many thousand tons of coal she had burned on the trip across?

"But what about the weather?" Cyrus asked. "If we haven't raised that cable and made the splice and finished laying it before mid-August . . ."

The officer shrugged. That was the chance they had to take. "One thing," he said. "You'll surely have good news about the St. Lawrence cable before we sail."

August 9, when the *Great Eastern* was ready to weigh anchor, the St. Lawrence cable was still not working. The little *Dauntless* was still shuttling back and forth across the Gulf of St. Lawrence. She was doing an excellent job. Congratulations from America weren't much more than twenty-four hours late. A telegram from San Francisco arrived at the same time as a cable from Alexandria, Egypt. Of course, it had taken the message from San Francisco much longer.

As the *Great Eastern* neared the rendezvous she plowed through high seas. Not rough enough to disturb the huge ship, but far too rough, Cyrus knew, for the ticklish job of grappling for the cable. Not quite mid-August, but the barometer was sinking, and his heart sank with it.

They sighted the *Albany*. The seas were too rough to send off a boat. They signaled back and forth. Good luck, the *Albany* reported, and bad. They had found the cable, grappled, caught it, brought it up several hundred fathoms, and buoyed the bight. Then—a storm. The buoy had torn loose. They had lost the cable and two miles of their grappling line.

"We can't do that too often," Mr. Canning told Cyrus. "We've got twenty miles of that line. Hemp and steel, tested to bear a strain of thirty tons. Strong enough to stand anything. But if we have to buoy the cable very often, and lose two miles of line at a clip . . ." He shook his head.

Monday the skies cleared and the seas subsided. On the *Great Eastern* they paid out their heavy "fishing line." Cyrus stood by Mr. Canning, watching the strain recorded on the dynamometer. One ton—two tons—five tons. That line certainly was heavy. After two hours the strain lessened.

Mr. Canning nodded. "We've reached bottom."

The *Great Eastern*, engines disengaged, began her slow drift athwart the path of the cable. Noon came. Afternoon. Evening.

At seven o'clock Mr. Canning said, "We've got it!"

The pick-up engine began its *chuff-chuff*. The five-foot drum revolved slowly. They could pay out their fishing line in two hours, but no one knew how long it would take to reel it in. An hour—two hours—three.

Mr. Canning shook his head. "It's gone. Reel in the line, check the grapnel, and lower away again."

By August 16 Cyrus had lost count of how many times they had paid out their fishing line.

Once again Mr. Canning said, "We've got it."

Cyrus lost track of the hours, too, before Mr. Canning said, "Easy now. Five or six more turns will do it."

Every man who could crowded at the bow, watching the line. The shackle chain on the grapnel appeared, then the eye of the grapnel, then the shank, and at last the flukes with what looked like a white-bellied black snake fast in their grip. It was plain that the cable had lain just half buried in whitish ooze, for one half was as shining black as it had been when it left the tarry coils a year ago.

At the sight of the cable wild cheers echoed over the ship.

At the bow Captain Anderson and Mr. Canning spoke almost together. "Watch it!"

But it was too late. The grapnel canted, and as it tipped the cable escaped from the flukes and disappeared.

In the heartsick silence that followed someone passed the word, "The barometer's falling."

They waited out the storm. They got ready to grapple again.

A fog descended. Day and night the blast of their foghorns signaled through white nothingness as they circled blindly and waited.

A calm day—too calm. Not enough breeze to drift the ship over the cable. They waited through that.

Wednesday, August 29, the *Terrible* closed in and hailed them. Captain Commerill came aboard. With an ache in his eyes he reported. He had been out four weeks; his coal was low. He'd have to return to Newfoundland to refuel.

"But as soon as I can I'll be back!" he promised. "Unless I've had word that you've got it in the meantime!"

"Of course!" Captain Anderson said.

Neither man said what they both must be thinking. August 29. The barometer falling again. If the *Great Eastern* hadn't brought up the cable before the *Terrible* could get back, she wasn't going to bring it up this year.

Friday, August 31. By now they had grappled—and failed—twenty-nine times. Despair was spreading like a plague through the ship.

Cyrus went to his cabin that night when he was too

tired to sit up, then lay awake because he was too worried to sleep. What was happening back in Newfoundland? Was the new cable working? And what of the St. Lawrence cable? Was it mended? Or were things still a shambles? Signals flashing from Europe in seconds, only to be stopped at Port aux Basques?

He gave up trying to sleep, dressed and went on deck just before midnight. He felt, rather than heard, a stir of excitement forward. Had they caught the cable again? He went to the bow of the ship. No one spoke. Motionless they stared at their engineer. Mr. Canning, watching the dynamometer, nodded.

"We've got it."

For fifteen minutes Cyrus watched. Why couldn't they hurry? Why couldn't they . . . I can't stand this again, he decided, and went below, only to find he couldn't stand that, either. He returned to the deck.

Eight bells. The fresh watch took over from the sailors on duty. One sailor shuffled a few steps aft, slumped on the deck, leaned against a reel of line, and closed his eyes.

Cyrus knelt by him and whispered, "They're getting along all right?"

"So far."

"How much longer will it be?"

The man scowled. "How the—" He opened his eyes, then grinned. "Oh, it's you, Mr. Field. How long? Ten—twelve hours, maybe—if we don't lose it again."

"This time," Cyrus said, "I have a feeling we'll do it!"

"That's the way I feel, too." But the man wasn't smiling. "That's the way I've felt every time. *Hurrah! We've got it!* Every bloomin' time."

Toward morning Cyrus went to his cabin. When he came topside again the take-up engine was still chuffing, and the huge drum turning slowly, inching the fishing line up from the depths. Ten or twelve hours, the man had said. But all afternoon the drum creaked around.

They were lifting and buoying in more than one place, Mr. Canning said, to ease the strain on the cable.

Night fell. It was after midnight—almost one o'clock Sunday morning—twenty-six hours since they had caught the cable—when the eye of the grapnel emerged from the water. Then the shank, and the flukes, with the cable caught tight. No cheers this time. Not a sound but the orders. The cable was in sight, but not yet safe. It was after two in the morning when the first turn of the cable wrapped around the take-up drum, and another hour before they carried the end of it to the test room, and stripped back the sheathing and insulation from the core, ready for the test.

Willoughby Smith attached it to his instruments, and lighted the lamp of the mirror galvanometer.

"Lights out, please."

In the darkness they saw the dot of light reflected on the white scale.

"Seem to have continuity," he said. "I'll see if I can reach Valentia." He signaled . . . waited . . . signaled . . . waited. The minutes ticked by. Five . . . ten . . . fifteen.

"Maybe there's no one watching the sixty-five cable just now," he said. "We'll try again in an hour or two. Maybe—"

The dot of light moved. Mr. Smith caught his breath. He signaled again. He waited.

Now, with the cadenced rhythm of Morse code, the dot of light swept back and forth.

"It's Valentia!" he yelled. "They're reading us! Perfect signals through the cable of sixty-five!"

In a moment bells, gongs, and buzzers spread the word. All over the ship wild yells echoed. Then guns boomed and rockets hissed and soared.

After the first cheers the men in the test room were quiet.

Cyrus wet his lips. "Ask them about the cable of sixty-six, and the St. Lawrence cable," he begged.

Mr. Smith nodded and sent the query. He waited.

When the answer came he dictated it, letter by letter. "B . . . O . . . T . . . H . . . O . . . K . . . They are 'Both okay,' Mr. Field."

Cyrus thanked him, turned, found his way to the

door, and went to his cabin. From all over the ship he could hear the celebration. Both cables working! The old and the new world joined! He locked his door, knelt by his bunk, and buried his face in his hands.

After a while he returned to the test room. He was glad it was dark. Crazy business—to keep your chin up for almost thirteen years—and then go to pieces!

As the *Great Eastern* neared Trinity Bay it looked as though all the boats in Newfoundland were there to greet them. They entered to shouts, cheers, waving flags, and twenty-one-gun salutes.

Captain Anderson smiled wearily at Cyrus. "Wouldn't it be fine," he drawled, "if we could sleep for a week before we have to be congratulated?"

Cyrus thought of that when he was home again with Mary. They sat in the library, watching the boys trim clippings that Fanny was mounting in a new scrap-book.

Fanny paused to read aloud from an English clipping, and Willie scowled. Why had Queen Victoria knighted five men and not their father?

Americans didn't accept foreign titles, Cyrus told him. The queen knew that.

"If you can't be a knight," Willie declared, "then nobody ought to be!"

If it hadn't been for what those five men did, Cyrus explained, there wouldn't be any cable. If Mr. Glass hadn't built it for them, and Mr. Gooch hadn't let them use the *Great Eastern*, and Captain Anderson hadn't commanded the ship, and Mr. Thompson hadn't figured out how to work long submarine cables, and Mr. Canning hadn't engineered the laying of the cable—

Willie scratched his head. "Huh. What *did* you do, anyhow?"

Fanny gasped. "Willie Field! You ought to have your mouth washed out with soap!"

But Cyrus threw back his head and laughed, then hugged the lad. "I was just the man that—well—held things together."

"Oh . . ." Willie went back to trimming clippings.

After a while Fanny said, "And if you think that wasn't important, just listen to this, Willie Field! This is what Sir Charles Bright said! 'Cyrus Field, to whom the world is as much indebted for the establishment of the line as to any man'! So there! And it's true, isn't it, Father?"

Cyrus did not answer. He was bending over the big globe, turning it slowly, pausing to span coast-to-coast distances of blue ocean between thumb and finger.

"I wonder how deep it is . . . the Pacific Ocean."

About the Author

JEAN LEE LATHAM WAS BORN IN BUCKHANNON, WEST Virginia, and now lives in Miami, Florida. She has a B.A. and a Doctor of Letters from West Virginia Wesleyan College, a B.O.E. from Ithaca College and received her M.A. at Cornell University. She brings a rich and varied background to her writing. Among other things she has been a linotype operator for a newspaper (during her undergraduate days), a drama editor, and a writer of stage and radio plays. During World War II, she was in charge of training Signal Corps inspectors, and received the War Department Silver Wreath for her work. She also was an American Red Cross Gray Lady for a number of years.

Her plays have been produced on such programs as "First Nighter," "Grand Central Station," and the "Kraft Television Theatre."

Of her family, Miss Latham says: "I believe the most important thing here is that I come of large and loving clans on both sides of the house; from vigorous people who like to do things with their heads as well as their hands; of one part of my family it has been said, 'The only way to kill them is to cut off the head and throw it over a picket fence in the dark of the moon.'" Her brother, Frank B. Latham, copy chief with *Look Magazine*, is also an author.

Miss Latham's hobbies are "anything in motion: biking, swimming, riding, dancing." She also enjoys cooking and listening to music ("anything from opera and symphony to popular"), often playing tape-recorded favorites while she is writing.

Miss Latham does extensive and painstaking research on her books and recently was forced to move into an apartment when her research material crowded her out of her trailer. In addition to YOUNG MAN IN A HURRY, her books include: THE STORY OF ELI WHITNEY; MEDALS FOR MORSE; CARRY ON, MR. BOWDITCH (winner of the 1955 Newbery Award); TRAIL BLAZER OF THE SEAS; THIS DEAR-BOUGHT LAND; and ON STAGE, MR. JEFFERSON!